Joni Rogers-Kante
SeneGence Founder & CEO

The SeneBlends Beauty Guide is a c[...] lets you learn about, and play with, eac[...] SenseCosmetics products available. This book is for all of the busy women in this world who need, and want, first-class makeup products that stay on and really work, and serve double duty in protecting and improving their skin. The longer you use the color and skin care, the more beautiful your skin becomes – I promise!

SeneDerm and SenseCosmetics offer unique benefits not to be found anywhere else in today's cosmetic industry. First, SenseCosmetics makeup contains the same amazing and effective anti-aging proprietary complexes found in SeneDerm SkinCare, blended with the patented long-lasting color technology of LipSense that stays on until you remove it. Not only do they not kiss-off, smear-off, rub-off, or budge-off, they improve the look and feel of your skin with each use, making skin more beautiful.

Second, because SeneGence products were created to be blended and layered together, each woman can have fun discovering her own unique look by mixing her favorite colors together, creating customized shades.

This guide is informative, as you will learn about all SeneGence products, from what they are used for and their benefits, to how to apply them step-by step. I also meant for this guide to be interactive! It is my hope that you will gather with your friends and have fun creating your own individual SeneBlends looks to suit your moods, personalities, preferences, and features. Enjoy learning, testing, creating, and playing with SeneBlends!

This book is dedicated to my SeneSisters of all shapes and sizes, skin tones and features, in all walks of life who have been on a quest for products that really work. The creation of these products and their distribution is my labor of love to you.

Choose to live life in love and abundance... then work for it!

Joni

SeneBlends Beauty Guide

6th Edition

Written by
Joni Rogers-Kante

Copy Editing and Art Direction
Jenelle Moad, Taylor King & Kirsten Aguilar

Design by
Tina Do

Contributing Distributors
Thank you to the following Independent Distributors whose talents, advice, and creativity have helped to make SenseCosmetics and SeneDerm SkinCare a world class brand of beauty.

Angie Rolke	Jeri Taylor-Swade	Renee Stewart
Barbara Harrington	Katie Sevenants	Ruth Scruggs
Bridget Lambros	Kaylen Young	Sharryn Rasmussen
Carol Douglas	Katie Sevenants	Sheila Young
Casey Davis	Kitty Wiemelt	Sheri Joyce
Cathy Rice	Laurie Weinberger	Sherry Henderson
Chris Mastin	Leanne Avant	Stacie Watts
Dawn Christian	Lee Blakeney	Stacie Contreras
Deb Sell	Leta Greene	Tania Leon
Deborah Mitchell	Lorita Prentice	Trish Langley
Deborah Perrin	Mary Ann Pinto	Zoanne Weaver
Frankie Jones	Pamela Bennett	
Heather Kalinich	Patricia Johnson	

2016 Lead MUAs of the Month

SeneBlends Makeup Artists of the Month are experts in SenseCosmetics application. From contouring with BlushSense, to creating alluring eyes with ShadowSense, they know how to do it all! Look for great "SeneBlends MUA Tips" all throughout the SeneBlends Beauty Guide from these 6 artists of beauty.

Cathy Rice   Angie Rolke   Sheila Young   Kitty Wiemelt   Tania Leon   Deb Sell

Contents

Introduction

History of Makeup

Cosmetics have been known to be used by women and men alike dating back over 6,000 years. But it wasn't until a century (or so) ago that the invention of photography and mass publication of printed materials, and especially film, contributed to an abrupt shift in attitudes regarding color cosmetics for daily use. As readers and viewers saw pictures of celebrities with flawless complexions and intense allure, the standards of feminine beauty began to change throughout the world. Cosmetics became a way to embellish one's appearance, hide imperfections and accentuate desirable features.

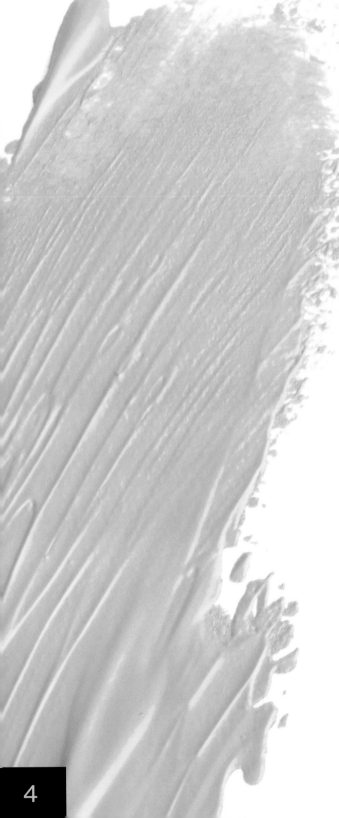

Here is a brief timeline of some of the giants within the cosmetic industry:

1900: African American entrepreneur Annie Turnbo begins selling hair treatments door-to-door.

1904: Max Factor migrates from Lodz, Poland, to the United States, and four years later to Los Angeles, where he sells makeup to movie stars.

1909: French chemist Eugene Schueller develops the first safe commercial hair dye. In 1910, he names his company L'Oreal.

1909: Florence Graham and cosmetologist Elizabeth Hubbard open a salon on Fifth Avenue in New York, and rename it Elizabeth Arden.

1914: T.J. Williams founds Maybelline, which specializes in mascara.

1915: Lipstick is introduced in cylindrical metal tubes.

1922: The bobby pin is invented to manage short (bobbed) hair.

1932: Charles and Joseph Revson, nail polish distributors, and Charles Lackman, a nail polish supplier, found Revlon.

1935: Pancake makeup, developed to look natural on color film, is created by Max Factor.

1941: Aerosols are patented, paving the way for hair spray.

1958: Mascara wands debut, eliminating the need for applying mascara with a brush.

1961: Cover Girl makeup, one of the first brands sold in grocery stores and targeted to teens, is introduced by Noxema.

1963: Revlon offers the first powdered blush-on.

1999: Joni Rogers-Kante opens the doors of SeneGence, offering the first 24-hour makeup that simultaneously stays on and helps make the skin more radiantly beautiful.

The Power of Color

Color evokes emotion. Color can make us happy or sad, confident or uncomfortable. It has even been known to decrease appetites, increase heart rates, and stir passions.

Light and dark play a role in how color is perceived, and thus, certain colors are more appealing during the day, while others look their best at night. Bright light makes color vibrant and alive, while shadows create depth. Taking all of this into account, colored makeup looks can be created based on mood, season, environment, time of day, and personal style.

Psychologists state that a lasting impression is made within ninety seconds, and that color accounts for 60% of the interpretation, acceptance, or rejection of an object, person, place, or circumstance. Because color impressions are both quick and long-lasting, decisions about color are critical factors in the success of any visual experience.

The human brain requires a sense of order to absorb a message from the object it sees. If too many colors or conflicting color hues are used, the viewer will become visually confused and the brain will reject the image. Additionally, boredom results if there is a lack of color. So, you can see how the right color combinations and color categories can be as important as the individual color.

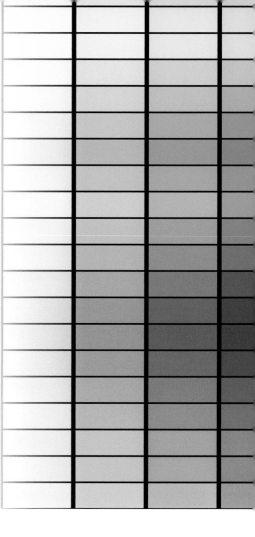

Colors also reflect traits and characteristics and can influence certain emotional impressions.

Red shades evoke: Energy, Love, Determination, Power, and Life.
Red is an attention grabber, can increase our appetite, and has even been known to increase metabolism! It spurs us into action and inspires our passions in life.
Personality Traits: Joyful, Passionate, Commanding, Loving, and Strong.

Orange shades evoke: Happiness, Confidence, and Resourcefulness.
Orange brings joy to our workday and strengthens our appetite for life. It connects us to our senses, helps remove inhibitions, and makes us happy.
Personality Traits: Enthusiastic, Happy, Sociable, Energetic, Sporty, and Self-Assured.

Yellow shades evoke: Wisdom, Clarity, and Self-Esteem.
Yellow gives us clarity of thought, increases awareness and stimulates interest. Yellow is related to the ability to perceive and understand.
Personality Traits: Good-Humored, Optimistic, Confident, Practical, and Intelligent.

Green shades evoke: Balance, Love, and Self-Control.
Green helps us relax. Green also cleanses and balances our energy to give a feeling of renewal, peace and harmony.
Personality Traits: Understanding, Self-Controlled, Adaptable, Sympathetic, Compassionate, Generous, Humble, Nature-Loving, and Romantic.

Blue shades evoke: Knowledge, Health, and Decisiveness.
Blue is a mentally-calming color. Blue has a pacifying effect on the nervous system and brings great relaxation.
Personality Traits: Loyal, Tactful, Affectionate, Inspiring, Inventive, and Caring.

Indigo shades evoke: Intuition, Mysticism, and Understanding.
Indigo strengthens intuition and imagination. It gives us a feeling of being a part of the entire universe.
Personality Traits: Intuitive, Fearless, Practical, Idealistic, Wise, and Truth-Seeking.

Violet shades evoke: Beauty, Creativity, and Inspiration.
Violet gives us inspiration for all undertakings and connects us to our spiritual self, bringing guidance, wisdom and inner strength. Violet also enhances artistic talent and creativity.
Personality Traits: Inspirational, Kind, Just, and Humanitarian.

Since all color is created from a blending of some degree, it makes sense that the colors in your cosmetics should have the ability to be customized and blended in order to create your very own custom look. A look that is unique to you, your style, your personality, and your presence, everyday.

Skin is Where Real Beauty Begins

The Science of SeneDerm® & SenePlex Complex®

SeneGence has developed highly advanced anti-aging skin care systems that help make every skin type more beautiful and radiant. Combinations of both natural and scientific ingredients provide proprietary formulations that are scientifically proven in a clinical laboratory to work on 100% of those individuals who use the products as directed. SeneDerm SkinCare Systems gently cleanse, moisturize, and protect skin with the proprietary SenePlex Complex.

SenePlex Complex is a Kinetic Enzyme that affects the way in which cells grow from the bottom layers of the skin to the top. SeneDerm SkinCare Systems can be used by individuals with all skin types and is available in three formulas to treat a range of skin types from: **Dry, Normal to Dry, and Normal to Oily.**

The active enzymes in the advanced anti-aging delivery systems work to eliminate dead skin and produce healthier, plumper cells as they move to the surface of skin.

That in turn increases:

- Moisture and Hydration by an average of **54.2%**
- Skin firmness and elasticity by an average of **51.9%**
- Luminosity by an average of **48.7%**
- Skin smoothness by an average of **45%**
- Collagen synthesis by **168%**
- And decreases skin sagging by an average of **25%**

Which results in:

- Reduced fine lines and wrinkles by an average **55.7%**

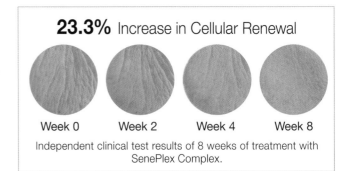

23.3% Increase in Cellular Renewal

Week 0   Week 2   Week 4   Week 8

Independent clinical test results of 8 weeks of treatment with SenePlex Complex.

By combining patented long-lasting color technologies of SenseCosmetics with anti-aging technologies of SeneDerm SkinCare and applying them to skin 24 hours a day, every individual, regardless of their skin-type profile, can achieve amazing results and a beautiful visage.

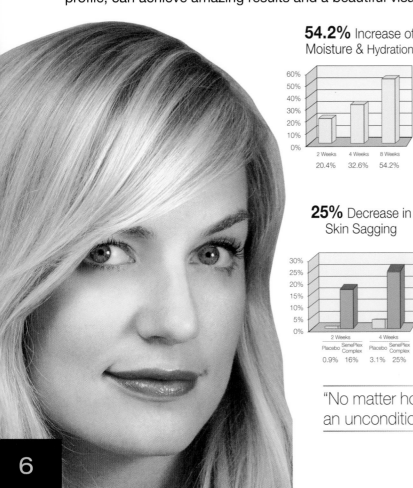

54.2% Increase of Moisture & Hydration

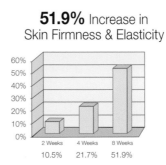

	2 Weeks	4 Weeks	8 Weeks
	20.4%	32.6%	54.2%

51.9% Increase in Skin Firmness & Elasticity

	2 Weeks	4 Weeks	8 Weeks
	10.5%	21.7%	51.9%

48.7% Increase in Skin Luminosity

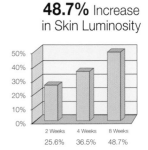

	2 Weeks	4 Weeks	8 Weeks
	25.6%	36.5%	48.7%

25% Decrease in Skin Sagging

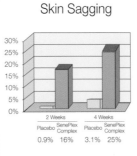

	2 Weeks		4 Weeks	
	Placebo	SenePlex Complex	Placebo	SenePlex Complex
	0.9%	16%	3.1%	25%

168% Increase in Collagen Synthesis

Over 4 Weeks			
SenePlex Complex	T Growth Factor	Lactic Acid	Retinol
168%	90%	10%	2%

55.7% Reduction of Fine Lines & Wrinkles

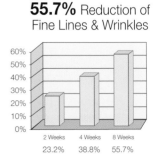

	2 Weeks	4 Weeks	8 Weeks
	23.2%	38.8%	55.7%

"No matter how much color you add to your face, it cannot hide an unconditioned complexion." -Joni Rogers-Kante

Skin Care for All Ages

Taking good care of your skin is a key part of staying healthy and looking good. Your skin serves many functions. It protects internal organs from the environment, it plays a key role in maintaining proper body temperature, and it processes some vitamins.

You should take certain steps to keep your skin in shape, so that skin may in turn, help keep you healthy. An easy to use skin care regimen can make your skin gorgeous and can be simple to achieve when using just a few products that really work. SeneDerm SkinCare is made to be used on skin of all ages. To create beautiful skin simply cleanse, moisturize, and protect.

Here are some guidelines that will help ensure skin is as beautiful as possible from one age to the next:

Teens & 20s – Cleanse, Moisturize, & Protect

- SeneDerm 3-in-1 Cleanser Normal to Oily
- SeneDerm DayTime Moisturizer Normal to Oily & MakeSense Foundation or Color Correcting Tinted Moisturizer
- SeneDerm Evening Moisturizer Normal to Oily
- SeneDerm EyeCrème

The teenage and young adult years are critical for establishing good habits to prevent skin damage that can lead to skin cancer and premature aging. Consistent use of an SPF 30 or higher, wearing protective clothing, and avoiding excessive sun exposure will pay off in the future. Color Correcting Tinted Moisturizer and SeneDerm Normal to Oily SkinCare products are great products to use. They include ingredients to fight bacteria, free radicals and help prevent acne.

30s & 40s - Cleanse, Moisturize, & Protect

- SeneDerm 3-in-1 Cleanser Normal to Dry (or Dry)
- SeneDerm DayTime Moisturizer Normal to Dry (or Dry), & MakeSense Foundation or MakeSense Advanced Anti-Aging Foundation
- SeneDerm Evening Moisturizer Normal to Dry (or Dry)
- SeneDerm EyeCrème
- Climate Control
- SeneSerum-C
- Collagen Night Pak

Many women in this age group begin to notice changes in their skin, including pigment irregularity (caused by both internal and external sources), fine lines and wrinkles, and loss of elasticity. SeneDerm SkinCare products contain SenePlex Complex and SeneShield to help combat these changes in the skin.

50s & Beyond - Cleanse, Moisturize, & Protect

- SeneDerm 3-in-1 Cleanser Dry
- SeneDerm DayTime Moisturizer Dry & MakeSense Advanced Anti-Aging Foundation
- SeneDerm Evening Moisturizer Dry
- SeneDerm EyeCrème
- Climate Control
- SeneSerum-C
- Collagen Night Pak

Women beyond age 50 will require additional anti-aging ingredients to help fight against the body's inability to produce younger looking skin. This group of women should use cleansers and moisturizers with extra moisture both day and night that help to control the climate around the skin. Additionally, applications of products that deliver beneficial additives deep into skin layers are a must.

"Beautiful skin can be possible at any age…simply."-Joni Rogers-Kante

Skin Evaluation Quiz

Having a healthy, clear, and radiant complexion is the first step to creating your own beautiful and balanced SeneBlends look. But first, you need to know what type of skin profile you have, in order to find a skin care regimen tailored to your individual needs. Use this helpful quiz to guide you in the right direction.

Instructions: Circle the answer to each question that best describes your skin.

1. How would you describe the level of oil on your skin?
a. No oiliness
b. No oil in "T" zone, but may be light oil in other areas
c. Oily mostly in "T" zone

2. How would you describe how your skin feels?
a. Tight and Itchy
b. Healthy for the most part, occasionally tight or flaky
c. Healthy for the most part, occasionally oily

3. How would you describe the overall appearance of your skin?
a. Tight, noticeable fine lines, red or rough patches, and visible flaking
b. Healthy appearance, clear with even texture, some tightness or flaking
c. Healthy appearance, occasional breakouts, can appear shiny

4. How would you describe the size of your pores?
a. Small
b. Small to medium
c. Medium to large

Now, let's analyze your results and find your unique SkinCare System!

🌿 Each product in all three formulas contains SenePlex Complex for increased cellular renewal.

If you answered mostly a: Your skin tends to be DRY. You need a skin care system that pours moisture back into your skin and helps control its humidity without being greasy, boosts cell renewal, and gently exfoliates away dead skin. Use these SeneDerm SkinCare products:

3-in-1 Cleanser Dry: adds essential moisturizers while protecting skin from moisture loss all day. Effective ingredients include:
- Humectants- bind moisture to the skin
- Sponge-Like Pillows- exfoliate flakes
- Sulfate-Free Foaming Agents- dissolve dirt, germs and bacteria

DayTime Moisturizer Dry: gives your dry skin relief and protection from the effects of heat, cold, wind, and water and keeps it hydrated and age-resistant. Effective ingredients include:
- Jojoba- promotes soothing and healing
- Moringa Oil- smoothes, de-puffs and moisturizes with radiance boosting fatty acids
- Almond Oil- leaves skin silky and non-greasy

Evening Moisturizer Dry: works as you sleep to pour moisture back into your skin and protect from evening atmospheric conditions such as forced air, cold air and free radicals. Effective ingredients include:
- Almond Oil- leaves skin silky and non-greasy
- Moringa Oil- smoothes, de-puffs and moisturizes with radiance boosting fatty acids
- Ginger Root- anti-inflammatory

3-in-1 Cleanser Normal to Dry: This cleanser is packed with natural ingredients to restore luster to dry areas and help restore and maintain moisture content. Effective ingredients include:

- Aloe Vera- soothes skin
- Avocado Oil- very rich moisturizer
- Lavender- soothes with anti-bacterial, antiseptic, and anti-fungal benefits

DayTime Moisturizer Normal to Dry: delivers vital oils and vitamins to bind moisture where needed most. Effective ingredients include:

- Aloe Leaf- helps to improve firmness
- Vitamin B (Panthenol)- helps new cells form
- Sodium Hyaluronate- for binding moisture

Evening Moisturizer Normal to Dry: works while you sleep to re-moisturize and repair cells damaged from exposure to dirt, sun, smog and other conditions during the day. Effective ingredients include:

- Avocado Oil- very rich moisturizer
- Vitamin E- essential antioxidant for maintaining healthy cells

3-in-1 Cleanser Normal to Oily: removes excess oil without stripping and drying, while controlling oil and killing bacteria. Effective ingredients include:

- Vanuatu Volcanic Ash- exfoliates dead cells
- Cone Flower Extract- promotes healthy tissue and collagen production

DayTime Moisturizer Normal to Oily: Oily skin still needs moisture and essential nutrients to protect it from harmful environmental elements, help control sebum, and reduce oil production. The powerful and effective ingredients include:

- Squalene- absorbs fat-soluble toxins
- Jojoba- promotes soothing and healing
- Allantoin- stimulates new healthy tissue

Evening Moisturizer Normal to Oily: works while you sleep to re-moisturize while helping to repair cells damaged by exposure to dirt, sun, smog and other conditions during the day. Effective ingredients include:

- Borago Seed Oil- powerful anti-inflammatory that reduces redness
- Vitamin E- essential antioxidant for maintaining healthy cells

SeneDerm Advanced Anti-Aging SkinCare

If you want advanced anti-aging results, add SeneDerm Advanced Anti-Aging treatments to your routine. These "miracle workers" are your proactive solution to halt aging in its path and leave your skin looking healthier than you ever thought possible.

All products contain SenePlex Complex for increased cellular renewal.

Climate Control: Contains small molecules that provide the deepest and most effective moisture to your skin. Climate Control helps even the driest, most damaged skin regain its healthy glow and moisture content. Its dual delivery system keeps the two key ingredients (SenePlex Complex and SelPlex), inactive and separated into two parts until shaken and combined. Effective ingredients include:

- Glucosamine HCL- natural anti-inflammatory that helps maintain skin's elasticity
- SelPlex™ Complex- a blend of herbal oil extracts and vitamins for skin repair
- Sodium Hyaluronate- restores damaged cellular walls

SeneBlends MUA Tip: "I call Climate Control and SeneSerum-C the "The Power Couple!" Pump 4-5 sprays of Climate Control onto the inside of your clean fingers, and add a pump of SeneSerum-C. Mix gently and apply to face, neck and throat. This helps to distribute the SeneSerum-C on your skin, and the Climate Control acts as a carrier. It's really handy for those that wear contacts and may choose not to spray the Climate Control on their face." - Angie Rolke, MUA of the Month

SeneSerum-C: A 100% natural blend of the most advanced anti-aging ingredients known today. This 'urbanization' defense formula is made for all skin types and works to repair damaged skin cells while helping to prevent further damage and create healthier, firmer, younger looking skin. Effective ingredients include:

- Stabilized Vitamin C – necessary for collagen production
- SeneShield – helps protect cells from immediate free radical damage

EyeCrème: This crème contains a rich blend of oils and vitamins that protects while working to diminish fine lines and wrinkles on the sensitive area around the eyes. The rich formula melts and emulsifies at skin temperature, creating a silk-like coating that reduces drag while applying cosmetics and replenishes moisture to the sensitive area. Effective ingredients include:

- Kukui Seed Oil- soothes skin
- Vitamin A- helps increase elasticity

Collagen Night Pak: A break-through anti-aging sleep treatment that harnesses the power of natural ingredients and the latest in skin care technology to seal in moisture while you sleep. As the final step in your evening skin care routine, it creates a protective veil that helps to prevent drying and damage that can occur overnight and can lead to unwanted signs of aging. Includes application brush.

- Plant-based marine collagen – works to restore and rebuild collagen
- Caffeine – rejuvenates and revitalizes skin
- Copper & Zinc – for antioxidant protection

Skin Facts

- Skin is the largest organ of the body. It has two layers: The outer layer or **EPIDERMIS** produces sebum which is oil that makes the layer water-proof; the inner layer or **DERMIS** has oil (sebaceous) glands, sweat glands, nerves, blood vessels and hair follicles.
- 30,000 dead skin cells fall off the epidermis every minute. These dead skin cells make up at least 90% of the dust around the house.
- Lighter skin tones have a higher tendency to wrinkle compared to darker skin tones.

The Art and Science of SeneBlends

SenseCosmetics™ with SeneDerm SkinCare: A 24-Hour Anti-Aging System

What is SeneBlends? SeneBlends is a color blending system using SenseCosmetics of various shades to create that 'one-of-a-kind' look for your 'one-of-a-kind' style in seconds from the privacy of your very own dressing area. SenseCosmetics were made to be blended together to create a myriad of unique textures and shades. Every woman wearing versatile blended shades of SenseCosmetics can look as though a professional makeup artist created a look that is just perfect for her color needs, skin tone, personal style, and mood.

SenseCosmetics combine anti-aging skin care with patented long-lasting color technologies to make looking beautiful and staying beautiful possible.

Not only do these incredible color treatment and skin care products deliver on their claims of long-wear and anti-aging results, but SeneGence offers the only color cosmetic line that has the unique ability to allow every woman to blend her own customized color products for custom glamour looks.

When used together, SeneDerm SkinCare and SenseCosmetics provide 24-hours of skin protection that makes any face look more beautiful, and keeps it that way for as long as the products are being used as directed. The ingredients are laboratory tested and verified by independent laboratory results. Through the use of a simple three-step skin care process and application of versatile anti-aging color cosmetics, the proprietary benefits of both are compounded to create a more beautiful complexion.

"As you are educating your friends and customers on the products, be knowledgeable but not too wordy; let your descriptions make the products sing and dance. Adjectives are very effective as you describe products they simply can't live without! And don't forget to use testimonials, they are powerful!" - Sheila Young, MUA of the Month

In order to achieve the most beautiful blends with your SenseCosmetics products, you need to have the best tools for the job in your beauty arsenal. Brushes are essential and are always better than fingers or sponge tip applicators. Wrinkles can be a result of constantly pulling and stretching the skin out when applying makeup with your fingers or sponges. As we age, our skin is already losing elasticity, and using brushes can help slow down this process. Brushes pick up less color per swipe and allow for better precision to determine color strength and vibrancy than sponges allow.

Blending is most effectively done with a brush because the bristles allow the colors to be subtly intertwined and meshed together. When choosing face and eye makeup brushes, it's important to find brushes that are not firm or stiff; you want the bristles to have a bit of fluffiness to allow you to sweep easily, horizontally, vertically, and angularly. Use a firmer brush for defining brow and blending eyeliner.

A brush for every type of makeup application with SenseCosmetics:

For the ultimate tool and brush kit, you need the SenseCosmetics Brush Collection.

1. **Stipple Foundation Brush:** This large brush features straight bristles that are firm yet soft, allowing you to perfectly apply MakeSense Foundation in a stipple technique. Stippling your foundation gives your skin the effect of airbrushed perfection.

2. **Blush Brush:** This fluffy brush is sized to perfectly shape the cheek bone. The medium sculpted head provides softness in application while offering durability.

3. **Contouring Brush:** This tapered brush is perfectly sculpted for contouring with BlushSense and MakeSense Foundation on cheeks, brow bone, and chin.

4. **Shadow Blender Brush:** Soften any look with this amazing blending tool. Perfectly blends ShadowSense on your lids.

5. **Shadow / Concealer Brush:** This oval tip brush gently blends shadows or creates a crease with ShadowSense. Great for blending concealers or highlighters in any area of the face too.

6. **Angled Detail Brush:** Define brows, eye shape or create detailed lining with this brush. This unique smudge tool is for adding depth close to the lash line and in the corner of the eye, or for brows. The long-handled brush has short bristles that form an angled tip.

7. **Detail Shadow / Liner Brush:** This brush features an angled handle and a long pointed tip to precisely place products. Use to apply ShadowSense as eyeliner.

8. **Brow & Lash Groomer:** Stiff bristles on one side to groom brow hairs and a metal lash comb on the other side to clean and define lashes.

Use the SeneBlends Blending Palette to create custom shades for each day's look. Blend creamy SenseCosmetics with one another, or the patented long-lasting technologies of LipSense for the perfect coordinating blends.

SenseCosmetics™
Brush Cleaner
by SeneGence®

6 oz / 170 mL

Caring for Your Brushes with SenseCosmetics Brush Cleaner

SenseCosmetics Brush Cleaner is the perfect product to effectively and gently cleanse your makeup artistry tools. Including a mix of scientific and naturally antiseptic ingredients like chamomile and cone flower, it rids your brushes of caked on product, dirt, oil, and bacteria to ensure that when you use your tools, you aren't brushing dirt and grime onto your face. It's safe to use on synthetic and natural hair bristle brushes.

5 Reasons to Clean Your Brushes Weekly:

1. Dirty brushes cause breakouts and irritation due to bacteria, oil and dirt accumulated on them.
2. Dirty brushes negatively affect color payoff of your SenseCosmetics.
3. Dirty brushes do not allow product to be well-blended or applied with precision.
4. Cleaning your brushes keeps them in good shape and prolongs their life - which protects your investment.
5. Dirty brushes can cross contaminate your products and cause them to spoil.

To Use:

Squeeze a small amount of Brush Cleaner directly into a clean cup. Gently swirl brush around in cleaner for 20 seconds (or longer if needed). Remove brush and rinse bristles well until water runs clean. Lay brush flat on a clean towel to dry. When brushes are dry, fluff them with clean fingers to reshape.

The Face

Prepping Your Visage

After you finish your skin care routine, the next step is preparing your face for perfectly smooth makeup application. MakeSense Silk Pore & Wrinkle Minimizer is the perfect base for your flawless face. It not only acts as a filler before foundation, but with time will reduce the size of your pores and minimize wrinkles.

To Apply:

Following your skin care routine, apply MakeSense Silk with clean fingers in a doward motion, and let dry, before MakeSense Foundation application. You will have a perfectly primed face and add an additional layer of anti-aging protection. Follow with Corrective Color Concealer.

When used as a concealer, Corrective Color Concealer should be applied under your MakeSense Foundation.

SenseCosmetics Corrective Color Concealer comes in two concealing shades to combat a variety of problems:

1. Green - Used to neutralize red tones on the skin. Use this for covering blemishes, red blotches, and rosacea.

2. Natural - Hides imperfections.

How does it work? Opposite colors neutralize each other: Yellow neutralizes blue (think under-eye circles) and green covers red (such as blemishes), while natural covers a multitude of imperfections.

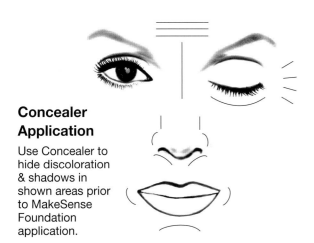

Concealer Application

Use Concealer to hide discoloration & shadows in shown areas prior to MakeSense Foundation application.

Hiding and Concealing with Corrective Color Concealer

The purpose of Concealer is to neutralize dark areas of the face, as well as hide skin imperfections and discoloration. MakeSense Corrective Color Concealer is the same formula as MakeSense Foundation with different color pigments added. This is why our technology blends so seamlessly! You can create an unlimited number of shades and tones by blending MakeSense Foundation with the Corrective Color Concealer.

To Apply:

Using a small amount of Green or Natural Corrective Color Concealer or a lighter shade of MakeSense Foundation, dab the product into the area in which you wish to conceal. Blend the product into the skin gently. Remember, a little goes a long way!

Tips on concealing:

- **Dark, Under-Eye Circles** - Yellow combats blue tones, which includes shadows and fine blood vessels near the surface of the skin. Use any of the yellow based MakeSense Foundations, ShadowSense shades, or Natural Corrective Color Concealer. Only go one-half to one shade lighter than the dark under eye area, as using too light of a shade will produce a raccoon effect.
- **Dark Spots** (aging spots) - Use a yellow based ShadowSense, MakeSense Foundation, Natural Corrective Color Concealer, or mix of those products.
- **Bruises** - Yellow, brownish bruises can be covered by using a violet ShadowSense as a concealer. Bluish-red bruises can be covered with Green Concealer.
- **Acne, red blotchiness, rosacea** - Use Green Corrective Concealer. If the blemish is raised or has a flaky scale over it, you must be careful to blend well enough so the green can't be seen.

SeneBlends MUA Tip: "When there are larger areas of redness to cover it's handy to use the Green Concealer. Mix a little with the foundation of your choice, and apply over the red area. Let set until dry, then apply the remainder of your foundation on top. This gives gentle all-over coverage." - Angie Rolke, MUA of the Month

SeneBlends MUA Tip: "On fair and light scars, you can apply Candlelight ShadowSense right into the dark area and lightly tap in before Foundation application to minimize the appearance of " - Tania Leon, MUA of the Month

Highlighting with Corrective Color Blender

In order to brighten dark areas of your complexion and give the appearance of radiance, apply Corrective Color Blender in White. White Blender can also be used to mix with MakeSense Foundation to achieve the perfect shade to match your skin tone.

To Apply:

Using a small amount of White Corrective Color Blender, dab the product into the area in which you wish to highlight and blend gently into the skin.

When used as a highlighter, apply Corrective Color Blender on top of your MakeSense Foundation shade.

Highlight

Use highlighter / blender or a light ShadowSense shade mixed with SeneDerm EyeCrème to highlight & open eye area

Using SeneBlend blending brush, begin application just short of bottom lash eyeline, blending down and fanning outwards into blush. Apply onto inner eye near nose to help eliminate deep shadows.

Tips on Highlighting:

- **Subtle Concealer or Highlighter** - blend White Corrective Color Blender with a drop of your desired MakeSense Foundation color before application; mix together, then apply on top of your foundation.

- **Under - Eye Bags and Puffiness-** Use White Corrective Color Blender or a lighter shade of MakeSense Foundation, and add on problem area. You might notice a slight shade on sides of puffiness, so add Blender there also, and blend softly.

- **Minimizing Facial Lines Around Nose and Mouth** - Apply light shade of MakeSense Foundation or White Corrective Color Blender in the deepest area of the line. Blend lightly up to highest point outside of line.

- **Chin** - For a small, thin chin, apply White Corrective Color Blender to the center of the chin, directly under the center of the lip. To minimize a full chin, apply bronzing color along the jaw line and blend it down, towards your neck. This creates depth and helps to strengthen the jaw line. If you do this technique, always apply contouring color on your neck to the shirt line to avoid a "mask" look.

- **Light Reflections** - White Corrective Color Blender can be used as an alternative to brightening with the use of light reflection to conceal imperfections and blur fine lines. You can also apply Blender lightly to the "V" on the outside skin of the inner eye. This will make the eyes appear to look brighter and wider.

MakeSense™ Foundations

Foundation serves three purposes:

1. Protects the skin from environmental elements.
2. Gives the skin a finished, polished look.
3. Supplies another layer of SenePlex Complex and additional beneficial ingredients.

Create a flawless finish and prepare skin to receive additional shades of the long-lasting, advanced color technology of SenseCosmetics with MakeSense Foundations, available in two effective formulas. Both are formulated with SenePlex and are the primary, long-lasting color products used as a base upon which to build long-lasting color technology, helping it to last throughout the day. MakeSense Foundations deliver a flawless, water-resistant finish, while providing non-smearing coverage.

MakeSense Foundations are available in 2 formulations:

- **MakeSense Original Foundation** - for flawless, long-lasting coverage and anti-aging, SenePlex protection.

- **MakeSense Advanced Anti-Aging Foundation-** formulated with SeneShield for advanced protection from environmental hazards and increased moisturization to help reduce and prevent signs of aging.

The uniqueness of MakeSense Foundations is not only in their content but also in what they do NOT contain. Ingredients utilized are mineral based and do not contain pore-clogging oils, emulsifiers, waxes, stearates, or sulfates.

MakeSense Foundations have the unique ability to be blended together in order to develop your custom foundation shade. Tones can take on warm to cool hues, depending on the color of your complexion.

MakeSense Advanced Anti-Aging Foundation

This powerful, creamy foundation is full of protective ingredients that help prevent damage to skin and work to shield from environmental hazards. A water-resistant skin care must-have, it is blended with moisturizers, minerals and vitamins with long-lasting color pigments that adjust to a wide range of skin tones to keep you looking beautiful and staying that way.

The exclusive blend of ingredients provides:

- Protection from environmental hazards with SeneShield
- A mechanical sun shield
- Anti-aging and moisturizing benefits
- Long-lasting, water-resistant wear
- Incredible coverage and silky texture

SeneShield

MakeSense Advanced Anti-Aging Foundation is formulated with SenePlex+ and SeneShield, one of the most advanced anti-aging and skin-protective technologies known today. Our skin is exposed to the effects of urbanization and daily hazards, like toxic pollution and UV rays, that can cause long-term damage. SeneShield's proprietary blend of powerful ingredients works to keep skin soft, supple and healthy and can actually help to reverse damage previously caused by exposure to daily toxins. Protect your face every day by including SenseCosmetics and SeneDerm SkinCare with SeneShield products in your beauty routine.

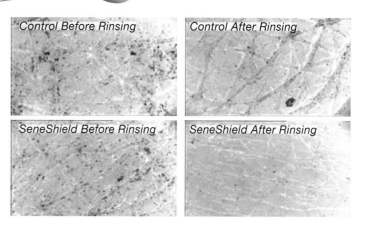

After rinsing, the control skin sample treated with SeneShield is the most radiant and clean, showing that the dirt and pollution did not absorb into the layers of the skin.

What is Urbanization?

Where has the pure air gone? Atmospheric pollution peaks are becoming increasingly common. Today, in many cities pollution is already a part of everyday life, to the extent that the sun cannot easily break through the smog, even in the height of summer.

Urbanization, or the effects of pollution, is intensified depending on the concentrations of pollutant substances and the frequency and duration of exposure. These effects range from simple irritation of the mucus membranes, to respiratory diseases, skin cancers or disorders affecting the nervous or digestive systems.

"Pollution can have dramatic impacts on the skin."

It can alter the skin's moisture-regulating ability, due to free radicals generated by pollutants. When put to such a harsh test, the skin barrier can lose its integrity and dry out. Asphyxiated or even intoxicated, the skin can lose its radiance and take on a muddy complexion. The first signs of inflammation quickly appear through redness and tingling. Pollution can also be responsible for the significant rise in the number of sensitive or reactive skin types amongst urban populations.

Protect your skin from urbanization with products containing SeneShield: MakeSense Advanced Anti-Aging Foundation and SeneSerum-C.

Finally, because of the hole in the ozone layer, the concentration of U.V. (ultra violet) radiations reaching the surface of the Earth is constantly increasing. Now, ever-present U.V. radiations are no longer only a summer hazard. They partner in damage with free radicals and can threaten the body's biological stability and its integrity.

15

MakeSense Original Foundation

This oil-free, water-proof and long-lasting liquid foundation can be used on any skin type and provides a mechanical shield equivalent to an SPF 30 when applied after SeneDerm DayTime Moisturizer. Each shade can be used on a multitude of skin tones as it adapts to your skin pigmentation.

Apply MakeSense Foundation lightly or heavily:

Lighter Coverage

- Apply foundation in a downward motion to minimize impact of facial hair.
- Place most amount of foundation on problem areas only; blend out with brush.
- Lightly blend foundation on face; make sure to blend around and under the jawline, into the hairline, onto earlobes, and around the nose.

Heavier Coverage

- Apply Foundation on face so no skin is visible through foundation.
- If one area needs more concentration of coverage, apply with a dabbing touch with your fingertip or stipple brush.
- You can also cover freckles and birthmarks with the dabbing technique.

Using a foundation brush is the preferred application method, because it allows for better blending and more even, softer-finished coverage. For an airbrushed look, use a stipple brush.

MakeSense is available in shades for all complexions:

Light

Porcelain (Light yellow undertones; for fair skin)

Ivory (Light pink undertones; for light skin)

Creme Beige (Neutral to light yellow undertones)

Light to Medium Shades

Beige Chiffon (Light to medium yellow undertones)

Medium

Dewy (Neutral undertones)

Fawn (Medium yellow undertones)

Almond (Medium pink undertones)

Medium to Dark Shades

Tan (Medium to dark yellow undertones)

Suede (Olive yellow undertones)

Cafe au Lait (Medium to dark red undertones)

Dark

Chestnut (Neutral to dark red undertones)

Mahogany (Dark red undertones)

Mink (Neutral to dark yellow undertones)

"It blends smoothly into the skin, protects from UV rays, sets, stays and makes me look great! What more can you ask for in a Foundation? "- Michele

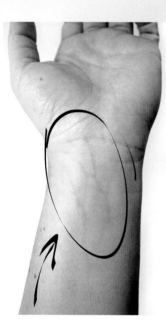

How to Find Your Undertone

You are either cool, warm, or neutral. Take a closer look at the veins on the underside of your wrist.

Are they blue or purple? If so, then you are cool, and will look good in MakeSense shades with pink or red undertones, such as Ivory, Almond, Chestnut, Café Au Lait, and Mahogony.

Are they green or olive? If yes, you are warm, and will look great in MakeSense shades with yellow undertones, such as Porcelain, Creme Beige, Beige Chiffon, Tan, Suede, and Mink and Fawn.

If you can't quite tell, then you are neutral, and Dewy will most likely look best on you.

Another way to tell is by taking a look at jewelry. If gold complements you best, then you are most likely warm-toned, and if silver looks great on you, you are cool. If both look equally fabulous, you are neutral.

MakeSense Color Correcting Tinted Moisturizer

MakeSense Color Correcting (CC) Tinted Moisturizer is the 1-step solution for healthy, beautiful, and natural looking skin. It is a lighter alternative to MakeSense Foundation and offers so many skin benefits.

Smooth this lightweight cream onto your skin and be instantly transformed. Enjoy 10 incredible benefits in one easy step:

1. Anti-Aging
2. Evens tone and texture
3. Blurs blemishes and imperfections
4. Kills free radicals
5. Hydrates all day
6. Anti-Oxidant rich
7. Corrects redness and discoloration
8. Lightweight, breathable formula
9. Protects with a mechanical shield
10. Good for all skin types, including acne prone

MakeSense CC Tinted Moisturizer comes in Light and Medium shades to match a variety of skin tones.

BlushSense™

BlushSense provides the perfect touch of creamy long-lasting color to highlight, define, or contour your cheeks. BlushSense is available in many beautiful shades that complement any skin tone. Use to blush the cheeks, and if desired, to create a sun-kissed, healthy glow in other areas of the face. As with all creamy SenseCosmetics, BlushSense is fully blendable with all MakeSense Foundation shades.

The powerful and effective ingredients include:

- SenePlex Complex- increases cellular renewal
- Yeast Extract- promotes new cell formation
- Orchid Flower Extract- powerful anti-oxidant with free-radical protection and moisture

To Apply:

Healthy and glowing are the looks you want to achieve when applying blush. BlushSense should be applied by placing one to three dots of color from the bottom of your cheek bone, back toward your ear. Using a brush, blend the color downwards in a "C" shape on your cheek.

Tips on using BlushSense

- BlushSense is specifically formulated to be used over MakeSense Foundation.
- Start with a VERY SMALL AMOUNT on your cheek or makeup brush. You can always add more.
- Look into the mirror and smile. The fleshy, lifted part of your cheek (the apple) is the best and most natural place to begin applying.
- Blend downward in order not to lift and highlight the fine follicles of hair on your cheek.
- With White Corrective Color Blender, all of the colors can be turned into softer, lighter shades.
- Mix any BlushSense shade with DayTime Moisturizer for even easier application and a tinted cheek look.

Common Blush Mistakes:

- Using too much color in too many places. For the most part, keep the blush on the cheek where it is most natural. Use very lightly on tip of your nose and center of your chin. Because of this advanced technology you do not need as much as powdered blush products.
- Applying in racing stripe line from the cheek to the ear can look dated. Ease the color softly onto the fleshy part of the cheek. This will look natural.
- Clashing with lip colors. It is safer to keep the cools and warms together.
- Bad lights. Remember to check your whole finished look in the natural daylight if possible. Some lights are dull and give the illusion of being well blended.

Blush Placement

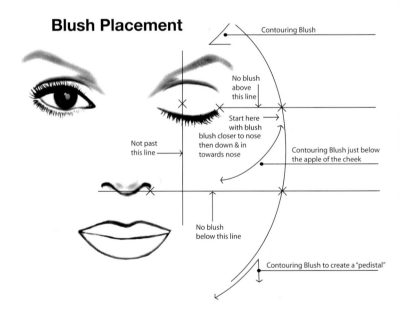

Contouring Blush

No blush above this line

Start here with blush blush closer to nose then down & in towards nose

Not past this line

Contouring Blush just below the apple of the cheek

No blush below this line

Contouring Blush to create a "pedistal"

SeneBlends MUA Tip: "Do you need a pink blush color in between Pouty Pink and Toasted Rose? Mix Pink Posey Shadowsense with your Foundation shade or Pearlizer, then apply to cheeks for the perfect rosy pink hue." – Cathy Rice, MUA of the Month

Final Touches: MakeSense Pearlizer and Translucid Powder & Bronzer

For luminosity, apply MakeSense Pearlizer. This adds a radiant, glowing finish. Mix it with your favorite MakeSense Foundation or BlushSense shade, or lightly layer after makeup application with a brush. Or for a natural look, use MakeSense Pearlizer alone, without MakeSense Foundation. It can also be applied on top of or blended into ShadowSense, or as an eye shadow itself.

For beauty on-the-go and effortless application, try Translucid Powder in Natural, Bronze Dust, or Silver Rose. It clots shine and absorbs oil and perspiration, all without drying the skin. The finish also acts as a mechanical shield to protect your skin throughout the day. Just lightly sweep on for a beautiful finish. Effective ingredients include:

- Acetyl Hexapeptide 3- plant derived amino acid and anti-wrinkle ingredient
- Allantoin- stimulates healthy tissue formation
- Talc- absorbs oil

SeneBlends MUA Tip: "Use Pearlizer to get younger looking skin! Blend a very small drop of Pearlizer into Foundation before applying it to your face. This gives just a tiny bit of glow to the skin and gives it a younger, dewy appearance." – Deb Sell, MUA of the Month

SeneBlends MUA Tip: "I love putting Pearlizer above and under eyebrows to raise the eye, on the top of cheekbones to highlight, and in the 'cupid's bow' on top of lips, for a full, pouty effect. Pearlizer is truly a fantastic highlighting tool!" - Kitty Wiemelt, MUA of the Month

Creating the Perfect Canvas by Contouring with SenseCosmetics

1. Dark Diminishes
- Highlight face by contouring outer triangle with MakeSense Foundation in a dark shade. Blend into earlobes and hairline.

2. Light Pops
- Apply light shade of MakeSense Foundation or White Corrective Color Concealer/Blender as highlighter in middle of face. Blend onto neck.

3. Highlight Eyes & Lift Cheek Bones
- The Triangle - Use White Corrective Color Blender or MakeSense Pearlizer to sweep under your eye, blending it down to a soft point to form a triangle under your eye and onto your cheek. This will highlight your eyes and cheekbones.

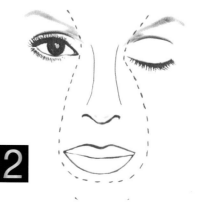

Contouring Continued

1. Cheek Bone Contouring

- Hallow cheek bones with a warm, bronze shade of BlushSense or MakeSense Foundation. Draw imaginary line from top of ear to corner of mouth. Blend into hairline.

2. Nose Contouring

- Tip Turn Up & Thinner Nose - Contour side and bottom of nose with a bronze shade of BlushSense or MakeSense Foundation.

3. Straight Nose

- Apply BlushSense or MakeSense Pearlizer to center of nose bridge using a blending brush.

4. Accenting Cheekbones

- Suck in cheeks, feel along cheekbone, tracing downward until you feel the natural hallow. This is where the dark color will be applied.
- Apply darkest color in deepest area, making a "C" shape from hallow, up to temple.
- Smile, and use a lighter color, lightly on apple of cheek.
- Blend lighter color on cheekbone into darker one.
- Blush can be applied lightly to tip of nose, forehead, and chin as well.

5. Blush for a Wider Face

- Suck in cheeks, feel along cheekbone tracing downward until you feel the natural hallow. This is where darker color will be applied.
- Apply darker color in hallow, making a "C" shape, blending softly down.
- Do not blush higher than eye on side of face.
- Use lighter color on top of cheekbone, blending it into the darker shade.
- Lightly apply tip of chin with lighter shade.

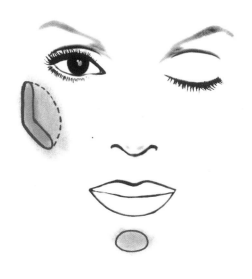

6. Blush for a Long Face

- Suck in cheeks, feel along cheekbone tracing downward until you feel the natural hollow. This is where darker color will be applied.
- Apply darker color in hollow, making a "C" shape, blending up to temples on side of face.
- Use lighter color on top of cheekbone, making sure not to work too high as to interfere with under-eye plane. This can make the eye look puffy.
- Smile, blend lighter color on apple of cheeks.
- Try a little touch of BlushSense on tip of nose for a sun-glow effect.
- A light touch of color on forehead and/or chin can help de-emphasize the length of the face.

8. Blush for a Formal Look

- Apply BlushSense on your cheekbone, sweeping down and back.
- Lightly apply BlushSense in the hallows of your cheek, making sure to blend well.

Have fun mixing the colors. Remember less is more. Don't forget to smile when you look into the mirror. It can truly take your stress away!

7. Blush for a Natural Look

- Suck in cheeks, and apply a darker shade of BlushSense, making a "C" shape and blending.
- Apply a lighter shade of BlushSense on the cheekbone, blending well into the "C" shape.
- Apply light blush down the center of your nose in a straight line. A little goes a long way, so apply very lightly.
- Lightly dab light shade onto center of forehead and chin.

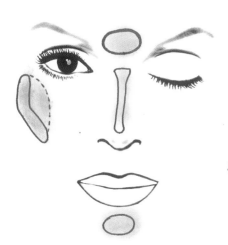

The 8-piece SenseCosmetics Brush Collection is perfect for blending and contouring.

Eyes are the Window to Your Soul

BrowSense™

If eyes are the window to the soul, eyebrows are the curtains or frames that define the entire eye area. Definition and color play a vital role in the look of your eye area. While brows can be thick or thin, definition and color cannot be overlooked.

BrowSense uses a two-step delivery system to apply color, then brush through brows for a natural appearance that won't melt or rub off.

To Apply:

Using short hair-like strokes, apply BrowSense to your brow, then brush out using the opposite end of the wand. Choose a color closest to your hair/brow color for the most natural look.

Brow Lift

- Using the tapered BrowSense brush applicator, apply BrowSense to the outer side of the brow line over the arch of the eyebrows.

To Thicken Thin Eyebrows:

- Eyebrow should begin parallel to inner corner of eye, and end just beyond eye.
- Eyebrow should be fullest at nose bridge, gently arch, and softly taper at the end.
- Start at bridge of nose and apply color over entire eyebrow area in short hair like strokes.
- You may extend beyond the natural line of your brow to make them look fuller.

For Full Eyebrows:

- The beginning of the eyebrow should be in line with inner corner of the eye, and end just beyond eye.
- For full brows, you do not need to go beyond the natural line of your brows. Rather, use a feather-touch stroke with brow color to fill in any areas with sparse hair.
- Blend with eyebrow brush.

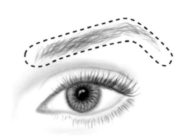

Brow Tips: To Tweeze or Not to Tweeze

- Most of us need to tweeze, at least a little bit to allow the brow to suggest a more finished look to the face. Besides the general rule of using a very good tweezer, it's a good idea to go to a reputable eyebrow professional at least once. It's worth the small investment to have her decide what's right for your face and establish the line for you. You can take over from there.
- To make it less painful, tweeze immediately after showering.
- Don't tweeze too often. Once or twice a week should suffice, as the idea is to control the new growth so the brows don't lose their shape too quickly.
- And Ladies… **NEVER* NEVER* NEVER* shave** or ever bring a razor near the delicate eye area! Shaving eyebrows can cause skin discolorations, and they never grow back the same.

Change your Expression with a Simple Shape

The shape of your brow is the framework for defining your desired look. Here are five simple and easy-to-remember brow arch designs that will help you make your perfect impression.

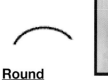 

Round

Makes the face appear rounder. It softens features and emphasizes the heart in the heart shaped face.

Soft Angled

Similar to angled, but its peak is softer, more subtle and feminine. Shapes like this have often been referred to as "perfect" brow shapes.

Flat

Perfect for those with a long face - its horizontal lines make the face appear shorter and more oval. A flat shape creates a very natural look.

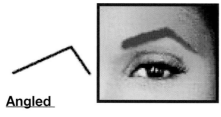

Angled

Great for those wanting a face lift. People will see you as more youthful and they won't be able to tell why.

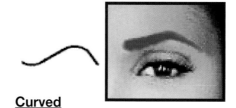

Curved

The eyebrow defaults here to a thoughtful expression giving a more professional look. This shape is lovely for all face shapes and should not be overlooked.

SeneBlends MUA Tip: "ShadowSense can also be used to enhance your brows. When you are filling in or creating your brow shape with ShadowSense (such as Moca Java or Garnet) and the color comes out too dark or you make a mistake, don't panic! Apply a little DayTime Moisturizer onto a cotton swab and gently wipe away, then restart. Remember to also apply your brow color to the upper portion of your brow to lift your eyes." -Tania Leon, MUA of the Month

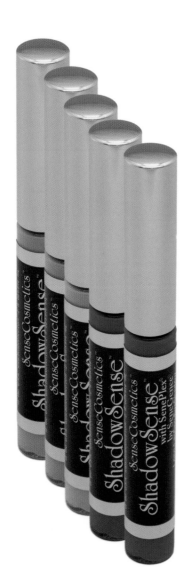

ShadowSense™

ShadowSense long-lasting and anti-aging eyeshadow is used to contour and highlight the eye area. Shades can be used as soft eyeliners, worn separately, layered to accent, contour and highlight, used as concealer, or mixed to create an endless color spectrum of possibilities. The unique formula starts as a cream color and finishes as a matte powder. ShadowSense is also available in a selection of gorgeous shimmer shades.

ShadowSense comes in a wide range of captivating colors, all of which can be blended to create a rainbow of shades that will allow you never-ending versatility and eye looks.

To Apply:

Using a flat SenseCosmetics blending brush, apply ShadowSense by placing product at base of lashes and spread up towards brow. Blend the product onto your lid using circular motions for soft edges and a natural look.

SeneBlends MUA Tip: "ShadowSense can also be used as concealer! With so many skin tones and variations of 'areas' we like to conceal, it's nice to use ShadowSense for somewhat heavier coverage without appearing caked. I've found great success with Candlelight, Whisper Pink, and Sandstone Pearl ShadowSense. Apply to desired area and gently blend. Let dry completely until set, then apply Foundation over. You could do this under or over your foundation, but I choose underneath." - Angie Rolke, MUA of the Month

SeneBlends MUA Tip: "Want to streak your hair to darken, highlight or give it a pop of fun color? Use our shadows for an amazing effect! Garnet or Moca Java ShadowSense can be used to touch up roots, and brighter colors like Amethyst and Caribbean ShadowSense are fun for adding streaks of temporary color." - Sheila Young, MUA of the Month

<u>**Eye Shadow Placement**</u>
Even Set

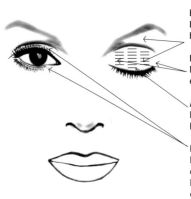

Base
Lightest shade at the base of eyelid to brow

Blending
Medium shade on the outer 1/3 of the lower eyelid, inner 1/3 of the lower eyelid

Accent
Darkest shade on the middle 1/2 of the lower eyelid

Eye Liner
Medium shade on the outer 2/3 upper eyelid, and below 2/3 of the bottom lashes beginning at the outer corner to the inner corner

Wide Set

Base
Lightest shade at the base of the eyelid to brow

Blending
Medium shade on the outer 1/2 of the lower lid

Accent
Darkest shade on the inner 1/2 of the lower lid

Eye Liner
Darkest shade 1/2 outer upper eyelid, below 3/4 of the bottom lash beginning at the outer corner to the inner corner

Close Set

Base
Lightest shade at the base of the eyelid to brow

Blending
Medium shade on the inner 1/2 of the lower lid

Accent
Darkest shade on the outer 1/2 of the lower lid

Eye Liner
Medium shade on the outer 1/2 of the lower lid, and 3/4 below the bottom lashes beginning at the outer corner to the inner corner

What Colors Should I Wear?- Color Theory

Ever wonder how you choose eye shadow shades for blue eyes, green eyes, and brown eyes? Use simple color theory by looking at the color wheel. Choose a shade and then take a look at the colors that are opposite on the wheel – these will be the shades that complement each other.

Choosing ShadowSense shades based on Eye Color Basics:

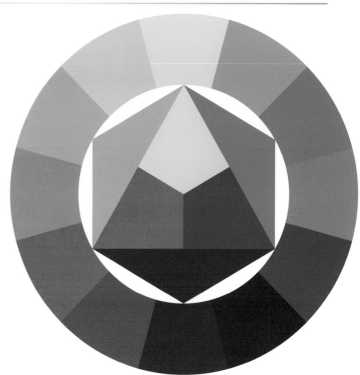

 Brown eyes: Choose Light Sapphire, Caribbean, Denim and Silver Violet to make the eyes stand out.

Green eyes: Choose Amethyst, Silver Violet, Pink Frost, and Mulberry to make the green look greener.

Blue eyes: Choose Sandstone Pearl, Moca Java, Copper Rose, Candlelight, and Garnet to make the blue appear even more blue.

Tip:

ShadowSense shades Onyx, Snow, and Granite will look equally good on all eye colors because they are black and white based.

"Create pastel shadow shades by adding Snow ShadowSense or White Blender into any ShadowSense shade. You can also deepen any ShadowSense shade by adding Onyx ShadowSense to it. Remember, darker colors pull the area back, while lighter colors reflect out." – Deb Perrin

Eye Color Chart:

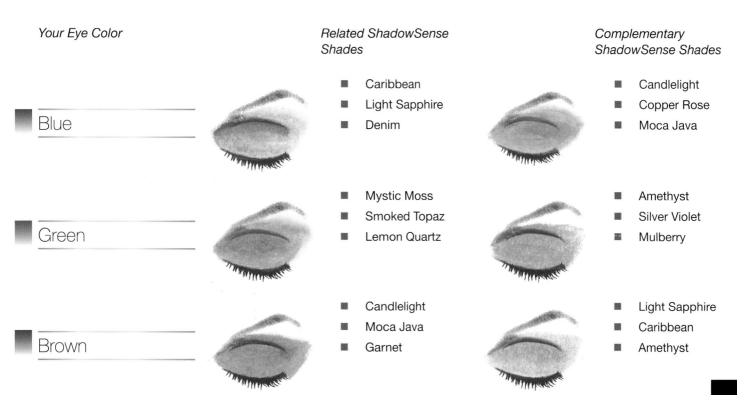

Your Eye Color	Related ShadowSense Shades	Complementary ShadowSense Shades
Blue	■ Caribbean ■ Light Sapphire ■ Denim	■ Candlelight ■ Copper Rose ■ Moca Java
Green	■ Mystic Moss ■ Smoked Topaz ■ Lemon Quartz	■ Amethyst ■ Silver Violet ■ Mulberry
Brown	■ Candlelight ■ Moca Java ■ Garnet	■ Light Sapphire ■ Caribbean ■ Amethyst

EyeSense™

EyeSense is revolutionary, long-lasting liquid eyeliner featuring waterproof, smear-proof, and budge-proof color.

This precise eyeliner defines and widens eyes. Simply apply EyeSense in a clean, sweeping line along the base of your lid.

To Apply:

Place tapered point of EyeSense brush at inner corner of eye, at base of lashes, and move towards middle of eye at lash line, in one continuous direction. If needed, lift brush from eye and insert brush into EyeSense for more product. Place tapered point of EyeSense brush at base of lashes and move towards outer corner of eye at lash line. Push EyeSense liner down into lash line with brush.

Proper application is the master key to shaping or reshaping the eye. EyeSense not only allows you to re-shape the eye but it also stays on until you take it off! With the proper application, you can accentuate the eye, change the shape and size, and make eyelashes appear thicker and lusher. EyeSense can even help create the illusion of more evenly spaced and set eyes, and of a perfect balance to the entire face.

EyeSense has the following attributes:

- Creates a smooth even line.
- Formulated not to run on or smudge under your eye.
- Ideal for a fine natural line, or a thicker dramatic one.

Tip: For a soft or smoky look, use a dark shade of ShadowSense such as Onyx or Garnet over EyeSense. Apply with an angled brush, and quickly blend or smudge for a smoky eye look.

Tips and Techniques for EyeSense

The purpose of eyeliner is to make eyelashes look thicker, and a dark liquid one highlights the shape of the eyes and deepens the look.

- Lining under the eyes is recommended only for those with big eyes, as it tends to make the eyes appear smaller.
- In general, softly draw a thin line along lashes, next to roots.
- Never apply eyeliner if your eyes are tired or infected.
- As a rule, it is smart to replace products that are applied close to your eyes every 3-4 months to avoid bacteria growth.
- Using ShadowSense as eyeliner is recommended for those who may be sensitive to the cosmetic alcohol in EyeSense.

"Don't forget to "blow" on the brush after shaking the EyeSense, to dissipate the cosmetic alcohol before putting on your eyelid. Dissipating the alcohol makes it less likely the liquid will tingle on your lids. The cosmetic alcohol in the formula keeps it bacteria free." - Jeri Taylor-Swade

Eyeliner Application Techniques For Specific Eye Shapes and Looks

Rounded
Liner: **Black Brown EyeSense**

Step 1: Contour along base of lashes

Step 2: Continue toward outer corner

Step 3: Thicken and wing line upward

Oval
Liner: **Black EyeSense or Onyx ShadowSense**

Step 1: Draw Line thicker in middle

Step 2: Do not line bottom lashes

Close Together
Liner: **Smoked Topaz ShadowSense**

Step 1: Taper line starting thick on inner corner

Step 2: Narrow through to outer corner

Farther Apart
Liner: **Garnet ShadowSense**

Step 1: Taper line starting thin on inner corner

Step 2: Thicken through to outer corner

Doe Eye
Liner: **Ebony Essence ShadowSense**

Step 1: Dot Liner close to base of upper and lower lashes

Step 2: Smudge with brush

Emphasize
Liner: **Black Brown EyeSense and Candlelight ShadowSense**

Step 1: Draw fine line close to lashes

Step 2:. Line top and bottom lashes

Step 3: Line bottom lashes with Candlelight ShadowSense

Wider
Liner: **Black EyeSense or Onyx ShadowSense**

Step 1: Line beyond beginning and ending of eye

Step 2: Do not touch lines together

Smokey
Liner: **Ebony Essence ShadowSense or Onyx ShadowSense**

Step 1: Line upper thicker than bottom eye rim

Step 2: Smudge both lines

Cat Eye
Liner: **Mystic Moss ShadowSense**

Step 1: Line top and bottom, and draw 'flick' on inner and outer corners

Step 2: Flick should be smaller on inner corner and thicker on outer corner

SeneBlends Eye Recipes with ShadowSense & EyeSense

Pink Bouquet
Base: Pink Frost
Blending: Pink Posey
Accent: Copper Rose
Liner: Black Brown EyeSense

Mystic Forest
Base: Candlelight
Blending: Copper Rose
Accent: Mystic Moss
Liner: Garnet ShadowSense

Silver Dollar
Base: Sandstone Pearl
Blending: Granite
Accent: Shine
Liner: Black EyeSense

Beautiful Bronzer
Base: Candlelight
Blending: Garnet
Accent: Smoked Topaz
Liner: Black Brown EyeSense

Angel Eyes
Base: Pink Frost
Blending: Mulberry
Accent: Silver Violet
Liner: Black Brown EyeSense

Tangerine Sunset
Base: Candlelight
Blending: Copper Rose
Accent: Moca Java
Liner: Black EyeSense

Pink Steel
Base: Pink Frost
Blending: Granite
Accent: Shine
Liner: Black EyeSense

Come Hither
Base: Caribbean
Blending: Pink Frost
Accent: Denim
Liner: Black EyeSense

Blue Jean Gal
Base: Whisper Pink
Blending: Copper Rose
Accent: Denim
Liner: Denim ShadowSense
By Independent Distributor:
Frankie Jones

Mod
Base: Whisper Pink
Blending: Pink Frost
Accent: Shine
Liner: Black EyeSense

Soft & Shimmery Night
Base: Candlelight
Blending: Copper Rose
Accent: Smoked Topaz
Liner: Smoked Topaz
ShadowSense
By Independent Distributor:
Cathy Rice

Soft Amethyst
Base: Sandstone Pearl
Blending: Pink Frost
Accent: Amethyst
Liner: Black EyeSense

Blue Penny

Base: Copper Rose
Blending: Pink Posey
Accent: Denim
Liner: Denim ShadowSense

Violet Dusk

Base: Whisper Pink
Blending: Silver Violet
Accent: Onyx
Liner: Black EyeSense

Beachside

Base: Sandstone Pearl
Blending: Lemon Quartz
Accent: Light Sapphire
Liner: Black Brown EyeSense

Neutral Beauty

Base: Whisper Pink
Blending: Moca Java
Accent: Garnet
Liner: Garnet ShadowSense

By Independent Distributor:
Trish Langley

Citrus Sunset

Base: Lemon Quartz
Blending: Moca Java
Accent: Mulberry
Liner: Black EyeSense

Smoke Stack

Base: Sandstone Pearl
Blending: Granite
Accent: Onyx
Liner: Onyx ShadowSense

Mother of Pearl

Base: Sandstone Pearl
Blending: Mulberry
Accent: Garnet
Liner: Black EyeSense

By Independent Distributor:
Heather Kalinich

Two-Toned

Base: Silver Shimmer
Blending: Gold Shimmer
Accent: Garnet
Liner: Garnet ShadowSense

Party On!

Base: Pink Frost
Blending: Smoked Topaz
Accent: Amethyst
Liner: Amethyst ShadowSense

By Independent Distributor:
Jeri Taylor-Swade

Brown Eyed Beauty

Base: Sandstone Pearl
Blending: Whisper Pink
Accent: Mystic Moss
Liner: Garnet ShadowSense

By Independent Distributor:
Zoanne Weaver

Toasted Glow

Base: Candlelight
Blending: Sandstone Pearl
Accent: Garnet
Liner: Garnet ShadowSense

By Independent Distributor:
Ruth Scruggs

Burnished Sterling

Base: Bronze Shimmer
Blending: Silver Shimmer
Accent: Gold Shimmer and Garnet
Liner: Black EyeSense

Contouring for Your Unique Eyes:

1. Hooded Eyes:

- Apply Moca Java ShadowSense with a SenseCosmetics Blending Brush. Draw thin line from one end of eyelid to the other between brow and base of eyelash; at inner eye next to nose curve line around eye socket curvature and along base of lashes.

2. Crêpe-y Eyes:

- To draw attention away from crêpe-y area, apply MakeSense Foundation over entire eyelid using a SenseCosmetics blending brush. Apply ShadowSense of your choice as a highlight to the top of eyelid just under brow.

3. Small Eyes:

- Use a light shade such as Candlelight ShadowSense on the inner three fourths of the eye starting from the lash to the mid-area of the lid.
- Apply a medium shade such as Moca Java ShadowSense, concentrating on the outer half of the eye.
- Apply EyeSense very close and very thin to lash line on top and outer corner of bottom lashes.
- Apply Whisper Pink ShadowSense under arch of brow bone to highlight and also in the inside corner of eyes to open up the eyes.
- Keep your eyebrows groomed and shaped. A more slender shape for small eyes will help to open them up.

4. Round Eyes:

- Use Moca Java or Mystic Moss ShadowSense sparingly on lid.
- Line under the eye with the same color to create a smoky base.
- Line the eye with EyeSense on top and bottom making sure to blend the shadow into the line.
- Create a more almond effect by extending the lower line a bit larger than eye shape and connect on sides of eye by blending.
- Apply LashSense on top lashes only, concentrating on the outer half of the eye.

5. Bulging or Puffy Eyes:

- Apply light shade such as Candlelight in the inner corner of the eye area.
- Wherever the eye is puffy or bulging, use a darker shade, such as Mulberry, in that spot.
- Line the whole eye with EyeSense to decrease the puffy effects. Blend well into the shadow.
- Emphasize upper lashes with LashSense, especially towards outer lashes. Use very little on lower lashes.

SeneBlends MUA Tip: "For hooded eyes, you can try the straight line technique: Find and note the highest point on your eyelid. Then, draw an imaginary line from the tip of your nose to the corner of your eye up to your brow bone. Draw a straight line with a darker ShadowSense color from the highest point to the imaginary line at the outer corner. This guarantees that the eye shape is going to wing up. Fill in the inner corner and under brow bone with a light ShadowSense shade. Blend, blend, blend!" – Deb Sell, MUA of the Month

LashSense®, UnderSense® & LashExtend

Long, full lashes add depth and dimension to your eyes. LashSense waterproof mascara coats and separates lashes evenly with long-lasting color, without smudging or flaking. The unique formula helps to build, volumize, and shape lashes while moisturizing to prevent brittleness.

Try UnderSense to build the fullest and most noticeable lashes. UnderSense is a lash moisturizing lengthener and builder. You may apply as many coats of UnderSense as you need to achieve a rich full lash. Allow each coat to dry before you apply a new coat.

To apply:

- Lightly stroke lashes from the base of the lash to the tip with UnderSense. For thicker lashes, allow the first coat to dry before applying the next. When UnderSense is dry, repeat the same application with LashSense.
- Apply LashSense to the lower lashes by holding the wand perpendicular to the eye and parallel to the lashes.

SeneBlends MUA Tip: "Curling your lashes takes 10 years off your age! Always curl with your lash curler BEFORE you apply UnderSense and LashSense. To make your eyelashes seem even longer, turn LashSense vertical (instead of horizontally brushing) and brush ends up."- Kitty Wiemelt, MUA of the Month

To improve the health and length of your natural eyelashes, use SeneDerm Solutions LashExtend. Results rival prescription treatments that cost over twice as much. Choose clear treatment for twice daily use. Effective ingredients include:

- SenePeptide- stimulates hair growth
- Chamomile Extract- anti-irritant with soothing properties
- White Tea Extract- powerful anti-oxidant

Tips:

- To give your lashes a sparkly look, you can coat the tips with ShadowSense Shine after LashSense.
- If you have wrinkles under your eye, do not put LashSense or ShadowSense on your lower lid, as this can accentuate under-eye wrinkles.

ShadowSense Shine & EyeLuminator

To make any ShadowSense look shimmer and shine, use ShadowSense Silver Shine over or mixed into any shade. It can also be worn alone for a natural shimmer. Also, to give your entire eye-area a luminous, glowing effect, use EyeLuminator. It's the perfect blend of SeneDerm EyeCrème and MakeSense Pearlizer, created to help make your skin more beautiful around the eye area. It brightens and highlights while moisturizing upon application. It will perk up your tired eyes in the afternoon too!

Makeup Tips for Glasses Wearers

Wearing glasses can mean that your eyes get lost behind the frames. When you apply makeup, you will want to focus on making your eyes pop. However, glasses do draw attention to your eyes, and can magnify any mistakes you make.

Check out our top tips for a glasses-wearing beauty.

1. Conceal Your Dark Circles

Glasses can often cast a shadow underneath the eyes, so concealing your dark circles is a must. Use Corrective Color Concealer in Natural, a yellow-based MakeSense Foundation shade, or ShadowSense in Candlelight to counteract the bluish hues.

2. Choose Eyeshadow Shades Based on Prescription

If you are near-sighted, your eyes will look smaller behind glasses and need to be widened. Choose light or bright ShadowSense shades such as Sandstone Pearl, Candlelight and Light Sapphire to make eyes appear larger, and line the top lash line and the outside corners of the bottom lash line with EyeSense. Be careful about lining all the way around the eyes, as this can often close them in. Use ShadowSense in Snow on the inside corners of eyes to widen.

If you are far-sighted, your eyes may look larger than you want. Choose neutral to deeper ShadowSense shades such as Moca Java, Smoked Topaz, and Garnet. When lining eyes, do not extend the line beyond your natural lash line. Also keep in mind the color of your frames. If you have colored glasses, you will want to be sure your eyeshadow doesn't clash with them!

3. Beautifully Lined Eyes

Help your eyes stand out behind your glasses by lining them with liquid EyeSense eyeliner. Extend your lines to make small wing-tips or cat eyes; this will help dramatize your eyes. If you have thicker frames, your eyeliner should mimic that with a thicker line. The same goes for thin frames.

4. Define Your Brows

When you wear glasses, it draws more attention to your eye brows, so keeping them defined and neat is important. Be sure to emphasize an elegant, angled arch. Use BrowSense to define your shape and arch.

5. Stand-Out Lashes

To help your eyes stand out more behind your glasses, make sure you are getting maximum impact by first curling your lashes with an eyelash curler, and then using LashSense with UnderSense. UnderSense will not only condition lashes, but it will help lengthen them before LashSense application. Make sure to really focus on lower lashes by generously applying your mascara.

SeneGence Distributor
Leanne Avant

SeneGence Distributor
Cathy Rice

SeneBlends MUA Tip: To make your eyes POP behind glasses, apply the lightest ShadowSense shade (or White Blender) to the INSIDE corner of your eye. Then, blend out with a small brush on top and bottom (towards the middle of your eye). Apply EyeSense as your final step." – Cathy Rice, MUA of the Month

6. Save Bold Color for Your Lips

Save those bright and bold colors for your lips! Want a pop of pink? Do it on your lips! Enjoy going bold with LipSense colors like Blu-Red, Fuscia, and Plum.

7. Don't Forget the Blush

Don't be afraid of blush if you wear glasses! Blush warms up your face and adds youth to your look. Be sure to place blush on the apples of your cheeks and blend down in a "C" shape. Remember to pick a BlushSense shade that complements your frames. For example, if you have red frames, a color like Cherry might compete too much with them. Keep color theory and balance in mind when choosing a blush shade to complete your look.

8. Smudged Liner

When creating an eye look, your main goal is to make your eyes stand out behind your glasses. Smudging your eyeliner is a great way to do this. Simply line your upper lashes and the outside of your lower lashes with a deep ShadowSense shade like Onyx, using an angled brush. Then, with an eyeshadow brush, go back and blend/smudge the liner for a smoky effect. People will be drawn into your eyes through your glasses. This is a great way to sport a smoky-inspired eye, without going all the way, as dark, smoky eyes can often get lost behind glasses.

9. Brighten Under Eyes

Brightening your under eye area will help counteract the shadow caused by your frames. Use EyeLuminator or Pearlizer under your eyes to help reflect light and fight the shadow.

Practice creating alluringly beautiful SeneBlends eye looks!

MakeSense Concealer

MakeSense Foundation

BrowSense

EyeSense

EyeLiner

EyeLining Highlighter

ShadowSense

Base

Blending

Accent

LashSense

Base

Tipper

MakeSense Concealer

MakeSense Foundation

BrowSense

EyeSense

EyeLiner

EyeLining Highlighter

ShadowSense

Base

Blending

Accent

LashSense

Base

Tipper

MakeSense Concealer

MakeSense Foundation

BrowSense

EyeSense

EyeLiner

EyeLining Highlighter

ShadowSense

Base

Blending

Accent

LashSense

Base

Tipper

MakeSense Concealer

MakeSense Foundation

BrowSense

EyeSense

EyeLiner

EyeLining Highlighter

ShadowSense

Base

Blending

Accent

LashSense

Base

Tipper

MakeSense Concealer

MakeSense Foundation

BrowSense

EyeSense

EyeLiner

EyeLining Highlighter

ShadowSense

Base

Blending

Accent

LashSense

Base

Tipper

Practice creating alluringly beautiful SeneBlends eye looks!

MakeSense Concealer

MakeSense Foundation

BrowSense

EyeSense

EyeLiner

EyeLining Highlighter

ShadowSense

Base

Blending

Accent

LashSense

Base

Tipper

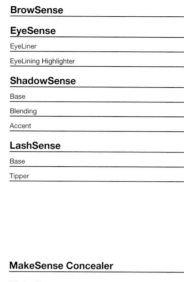

MakeSense Concealer

MakeSense Foundation

BrowSense

EyeSense

EyeLiner

EyeLining Highlighter

ShadowSense

Base

Blending

Accent

LashSense

Base

Tipper

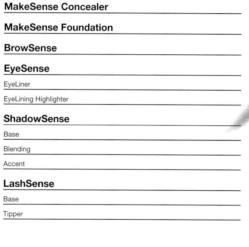

MakeSense Concealer

MakeSense Foundation

BrowSense

EyeSense

EyeLiner

EyeLining Highlighter

ShadowSense

Base

Blending

Accent

LashSense

Base

Tipper

MakeSense Concealer

MakeSense Foundation

BrowSense

EyeSense

EyeLiner

EyeLining Highlighter

ShadowSense

Base

Blending

Accent

LashSense

Base

Tipper

MakeSense Concealer

MakeSense Foundation

BrowSense

EyeSense

EyeLiner

EyeLining Highlighter

ShadowSense

Base

Blending

Accent

LashSense

Base

Tipper

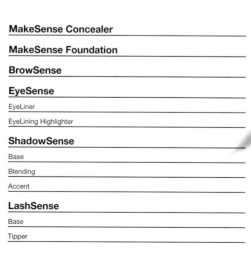

Lips Speak Volumes About Who You Are

LinerSense®

To achieve a full, rich lip, line your lips prior to applying your lip color. LinerSense has the same long-lasting color technology as LipSense, and blends, complements, lines and defines as the first step to creating the perfect pout.

To Apply:

Starting with your bottom lip, apply LinerSense in one motion beginning with one end of your mouth and carrying it to the other. Follow the same technique on the upper lip. If you feel more comfortable beginning in the middle of lips and lining outwards, you may do that instead. You may choose a shade that is slightly darker than the lip color you are wearing to create the desired look.

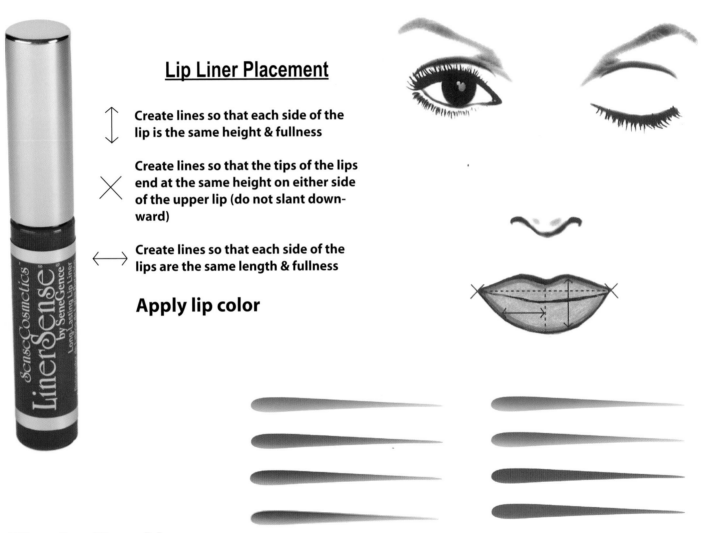

Lip Liner Placement

Create lines so that each side of the lip is the same height & fullness

Create lines so that the tips of the lips end at the same height on either side of the upper lip (do not slant downward)

Create lines so that each side of the lips are the same length & fullness

Apply lip color

Tips for Your Lips:

- A full rounded mouth shape is younger looking. Flat thin lips are harsh and strict. To find the ideal width for your lips, stare straight ahead into a mirror. Draw an imaginary line from the inner curve of the iris, down the cheeks to the lips. Anything that extends beyond this point should simply not be colored.

"I have tried every liner. LinerSense is the only lip liner that works the way it is supposed to. It lines and defines without bleeding." – Loni

Creating Different Shaped Lips with LipSense and LinerSense:

Changing the shape and color of our lips changes the expression of our face.

Tips for Your Lips:

- Remember to keep in mind the rest of your makeup when choosing your LipSense shade. If you are wearing dark ShadowSense shades, choose a more muted, lighter LipSense shade. If you are sporting a neutral palette on your eyes, go bold or bright on your LipSense. It's all about the balance.

1. Small Mouth with Small Lips:

- Take LinerSense outside of the natural lip line. Work slowly and steadily to form a perfect shape. Fill in with LipSense color. A LipSense Highlighter shade on the upper lip would also create an impression of fullness.

2. Large Mouth with Full Lips:

- Outline lips with a dark shade of LinerSense, just inside the natural contours of the mouth. Then, apply a layer of LipSense of a lighter shade within this outline. Use medium toned LipSense colors for the 2nd and 3rd layers and avoid dark browns, plums, electric brights or shimmer shades.

3. Full Upper Lip:

- Outline just inside natural contour of the upper lip with LinerSense and apply a dark shade of LipSense color. Then outline the lower lip just outside its natural contour and emphasize by filling in with a lighter shade of LipSense.

4. Full Lower Lip:

- Outline upper lip just outside its natural contour with LinerSense. Apply a light shade of LipSense color, and in the center, add a touch of Glossy Gloss. Outline lower lip with LinerSense just inside its natural contour. Then fill in with a darker shade of LipSense.

5. Wide Mouth:

- Cover the corners of the mouth with MakeSense Foundation or Natural Corrective Color Concealer. Use LinerSense to create a new lip line that begins a few millimeters before the corners of the mouth, and then fill in with LipSense.

6. To Even Out Crooked Lips:

- Cover fullest lip line or fullest lip line area with MakeSense Foundation. Using LinerSense color of choice, line lips on full side just inside natural lip line. Be sure to balance lips and soften lines for a natural look.

LipSense®

No glamour look is complete without rich, wonderful, lip color. The premier product of SeneGence is LipSense Long-Lasting Liquid Lip Color. LipSense is an amazing departure from conventional lipsticks and lip colors found on the market today, and comes in over 60 incredible shades. All LipSense colors can be layered together to create a countless number of shades that are just right for your exclusive look.

This unique, patented product is waterproof and does not smear off, rub off, nor kiss off! Not only is your look unique, but it stays put until you want it to come off (up to 18 hours), no matter what you put it through! LipSense has been a favorite for over 15 years and is loved by celebrities, makeup artists...and you!

"No other lip color can compare to LipSense: long-lasting and no smearing or running... EVER!!!!!" - Deanna

How to apply LipSense:

Apply to clean, dry lips. For a more defined look, line lips with LinerSense first. With lips parted, place LipSense applicator on lip beginning at the outside corner and spread in a fluid, sweeping motion to the opposite corner of the lip without lifting the applicator (do not move applicator back and forth). Use three layers for long-lasting results. Let each layer dry about five seconds before applying the next layer. Finish your customized look (any three shades) with LipSense moisturizing glosses – to keep your color lasting and your lips moist and plump.

SeneBlends MUA Tip: "Many of my mature clients have a purplish hue to their lips. It makes their lips appear darker and smaller. By applying a LipSense shade with a warm base, it counteracts that darkness, making lips appear larger and more youthful. A mature client whose skin tone is cool can still wear pinks, but they should be yellow-based like Summer Sunset or Apple Cider." – Cathy Rice, MUA of the Month

Picking The Right Shade of LipSense:

Lip colors that work best are those that have some of your skin's natural tones in their color:

Light skin and blonde hair: Most shades of orange, pink, purple

Light skin and dark hair: Most shades of brown and beige

Red hair: coral-red, brown and bronze colors

Dark skin and dark hair: Most shades of red, violet

> "Always wear stripes of LipSense on the back of your hand to "WOW" those you come in contact with." –Jeri Taylor Swade

LipSense in the News

LipSense is loved and used by many celebrities, makeup artists, and women all around the world. LipSense, SenseCosmetics and SeneDerm SkinCare have been featured in many national and local publications that have raved about the long-lasting and anti-aging properties of our products that really work. To see all of the press hits featuring SeneGence products, please visit the SeneGence.com "In the Media" section.

Do you get glam every day? "I can be at home in sweatpants, and I'll slap on red lipstick to write in my diary. LipSense in Blu-Red always seems to do the trick. It's kissproof."
- Christina Aguilera, recording artist

"I wear LipSense by SeneGence in Roseberry because it stays put - I only get a three-minute touch-up. Plus, it doesn't smear all over the mic!"
-Victoria Justice, recording artist

SeneBlends Lip Recipes with LipSense

SeneBlends MUA Tip: "It's fun experimenting with our amazing LipSense colors by using complementing or even darker colors to give a lined look or ombré look to our lips. While our LinerSense is fabulous, this LipSense liner trick is perfect in a pinch or when you are seeking a thicker line."- Angie Rolke, MUA of the Month

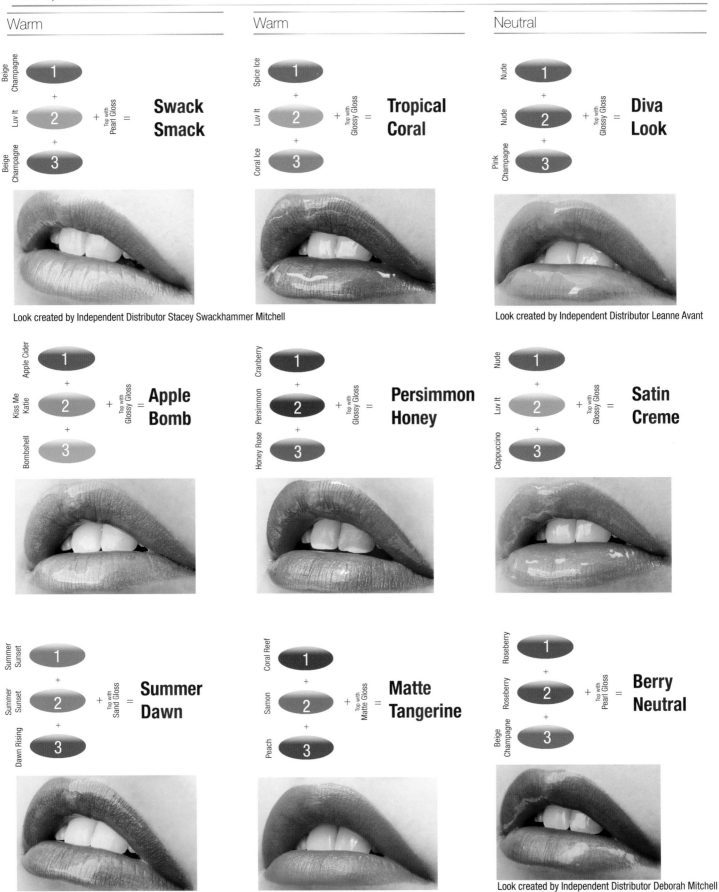

Warm

Beige Champagne **1**
+
Luv It **2** + Top with Pearl Gloss = **Swack Smack**
+
Beige Champagne **3**

Look created by Independent Distributor Stacey Swackhammer Mitchell

Apple Cider **1**
+
Kiss Me Katie **2** + Top with Glossy Gloss = **Apple Bomb**
+
Bombshell **3**

Summer Sunset **1**
+
Summer Sunset **2** + Top with Sand Gloss = **Summer Dawn**
+
Dawn Rising **3**

Warm

Spice Ice **1**
+
Luv It **2** + Top with Glossy Gloss = **Tropical Coral**
+
Coral Ice **3**

Cranberry **1**
+
Persimmon **2** + Top with Glossy Gloss = **Persimmon Honey**
+
Honey Rose **3**

Coral Reef **1**
+
Samon **2** + Top with Matte Gloss = **Matte Tangerine**
+
Peach **3**

Neutral

Nude **1**
+
Nude **2** + Top with Glossy Gloss = **Diva Look**
+
Pink Champagne **3**

Look created by Independent Distributor Leanne Avant

Nude **1**
+
Luv It **2** + Top with Glossy Gloss = **Satin Creme**
+
Cappuccino **3**

Roseberry **1**
+
Roseberry **2** + Top with Pearl Gloss = **Berry Neutral**
+
Beige Champagne **3**

Look created by Independent Distributor Deborah Mitchell

"With an array of 60 stunning colors, there are so many effects you can achieve by mixing colors and topping with the vast selection of gorgeous glosses…One thing is certain: with endless combination possibilities I'll be busy for quite a while, no doubt toying with my vast library of LipSense." - Shannon McGovern of beautyshallsavetheworld.com

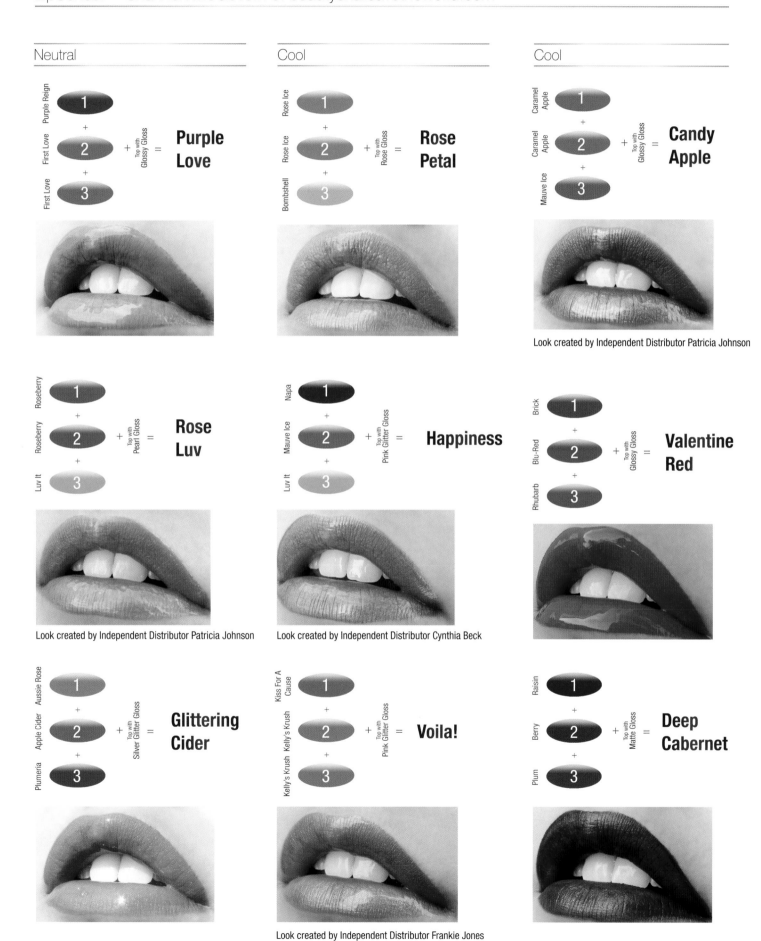

Neutral

Purple Reign **1**
+
First Love **2** + Top with Glossy Gloss = **Purple Love**
+
First Love **3**

Cool

Rose Ice **1**
+
Rose Ice **2** + Top with Rose Gloss = **Rose Petal**
+
Bombshell **3**

Cool

Caramel Apple **1**
+
Caramel Apple **2** + Top with Glossy Gloss = **Candy Apple**
+
Mauve Ice **3**

Look created by Independent Distributor Patricia Johnson

Roseberry **1**
+
Roseberry **2** + Top with Pearl Gloss = **Rose Luv**
+
Luv It **3**

Napa **1**
+
Mauve Ice **2** + Top with Pink Glitter Gloss = **Happiness**
+
Luv It **3**

Brick **1**
+
Blu-Red **2** + Top with Glossy Gloss = **Valentine Red**
+
Rhubarb **3**

Look created by Independent Distributor Patricia Johnson   Look created by Independent Distributor Cynthia Beck

Aussie Rose **1**
+
Apple Cider **2** + Top with Silver Glitter Gloss = **Glittering Cider**
+
Plumeria **3**

Kiss For A Cause **1**
+
Kelly's Krush **2** + Top with Pink Glitter Gloss = **Voila!**
+
Kelly's Krush **3**

Raisin **1**
+
Berry **2** + Top with Matte Gloss = **Deep Cabernet**
+
Plum **3**

Look created by Independent Distributor Frankie Jones

LipSense Lip Recipes

Practice creating special SeneBlends lip looks here! Layer three colors to create one-of-a-kind lip shades unique to you.

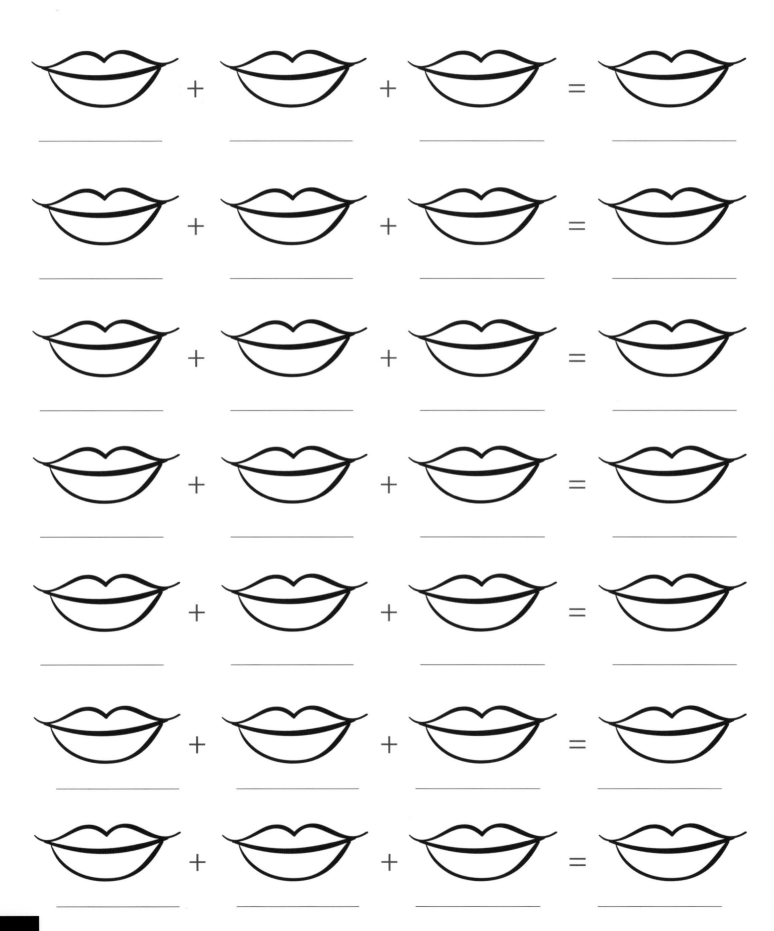

LipSense Gloss & Moisturizing Lip Balm

LipSense Gloss comes in a variety of different finishes to complete the look you wish to achieve and keep your lips plump and moist. Dehydrated and damaged lips are no match for the moisturizing ability of Shea Butter, a natural ingredient used as the base for the many textures of LipSense Glosses. They also improve the longevity of LipSense Liquid Lip Color, as well as cover and protect naked lips.

Tips for Gloss:

- To soften any LipSense shade, just apply Sand Gloss on top. The soft beige tint and understated shimmer will instantly mellow out the color of the LipSense.
- For an iridescent, cool finish, top LipSense with Opal Gloss. It will completely transform the color!
- For especially pouty lips, only apply Glossy Gloss in the center of the top and bottom lips. You can even hit the middle with a little Gold or Silver Glitter Gloss for an extra pop.
- Use gloss tones that complement the tone of your LipSense. If you are wearing a blue-based LipSense shade, top with cool glosses such as Rose, Silver Glitter, or Orchid Gloss. If you are wearing a yellow-based LipSense shade, top with warm glosses such as Gold Glitter and Sand Gloss.

"My lips were cracked and painful. I tried every waxy product on the market with only painful results. Then I found LipSense Gloss. Within one week my lips were relieved. I have not had dry lips for almost eight years now. I love my Glossy Gloss." - Crystal

"When using Glitter Gloss, first put a layer of Glossy Gloss on to keep the glitter particles from rubbing against the LipSense. This will help your LipSense color to stay on even longer." - Jeri Taylor-Swade

LipSense Moisturizing Lip Balm

Smooth on this long-lasting, nourishing balm with moisture-rich botanicals such as Coconut Oil, Cocoa and Shea butters, and Orchid Flower extract to help bind hydration to lips. The addition of SenePlex Complex provides anti-aging and restorative benefits. This lightweight formula is fragrance-free with a matte finish: perfect for everyone.

2 layers Samon and 1 layer Kiss For A Cause LipSense topped with Orchid Gloss

Tip:

- LipSense Lip Balm is not meant to be worn over LipSense. Apply Lip Balm to clean lips. For soft lips when you wake up in the morning, apply Lip Balm before you go to sleep, and let the botanicals and SenePlex Complex protect and moisturize your lips over night.

Unique Tattoo Cover Up Solutions

Water-proof, long-lasting SenseCosmetics are so versatile, they can even temporarily cover permanent tattoos.

"The right LipSense shade, paired with MakeSense Foundation, can effectively make a tattoo disappear. This is a great technique to use for someone who wants a quick cover up solution, like for a special event. It's easy to do, doesn't feel caked on, and works great."- Renee Stewart

To cover dark or black tattoos:

In order to effectively cover up a dark tattoo, you need to neutralize its tone first. To do this, completely cover the tattoo in one or two layers of a dark red LipSense shade, such as Red Cherry or Brick, and let it dry completely. Then, apply several thin layers of MakeSense Foundation to match the skin tone. Set the entire area with Translucid Powder in Natural. The tattoo will vanish!

To cover light tattoos:

The process for covering up light tattoos is the same except for the LipSense shade used underneath. Completely cover the tattoo with one or two layers of a light mauve shade such as Praline Rose. Then, follow with MakeSense Foundation and Natural Translucid Powder. Voila, gone!

Tattoo Cover-Up Kit:

Tattoo partially covered with Praline Rose LipSense, MakeSense Foundation, and set with Natural Translucid Powder.

Tip:

If you don't want to cover up a tattoo, try highlighting it. This technique is easy, but has major impact! To highlight a tattoo, download some ShadowSense Shine onto a brush, and trace the tattoo, making sure to blend the product. Apply more on areas you want to emphasize. The fine glitter particles will highlight and make the tattoo shine!

SeneBlends MUA Tip: "Here's a fun tip for those with children: Do some face painting! Create a temporary 'tattoo' with ShadowSense, BlushSense or any of the creamy SenseCosmetics. They are gentle on skin and won't rub off on clothes or furniture. This is a fun reward for clean rooms, good grades, or kind behavior. If you are not artistic, get some ideas online, or even easier- use a stencil. This is also a good fund raiser for carnivals and children's parties." - Sheila Young, MUA of the Month

Blend-It! Signature SeneBlends Looks

These Signature SeneBlends looks were created to give you inspiration for creating a complete glamour look for your visage. They are divided into blue-based (cool), neutral, and yellow-based (warm) to complement an array of skin tones, preferences, and styles.

SeneChic/Blue-Based

MakeSense™ Foundation	**Match to skin tone**
BlushSense™	**Pouty Pink**
BrowSense®	**Match to brow color**
EyeSense™	**Black**
LashSense®	**Black**
ShadowSense™	**Whisper Pink/ Moca Java/ Ebony Essence**
LinerSense®	**Blu-Red**
LipSense®	**Rhubarb**
LipSense® Highlighter	**Rose Ice**
Moisturizing Gloss	**Silver Glitter Gloss**

SeneNeutral/Neutral

MakeSense™ Foundation	**Match to skin tone**
BlushSense™	**Toasted Rose**
BrowSense®	**Match to brow color**
EyeSense™	**Black**
LashSense®	**Black**
ShadowSense™	**Silver Violet/ Mulberry/ Denim**
LinerSense®	**Dark Raisin**
LipSense®	**Nude**
Moisturizing Gloss	**Glossy**

SeneGlow/ Yellow-Based

MakeSense™ Foundation	**Match to skin tone**
BlushSense™	**Terra Cotta**
BrowSense®	**Match to brow color**
EyeSense™	**Black Brown**
LashSense®	**Brown**
ShadowSense™	**Candlelight/ Copper Rose**
LinerSense®	**Neutral**
LipSense®	**Cappuccino**
LipSense® Highlighter	**Spice Ice**
Moisturizing Gloss	**Gold Glitter**

Practice creating your own complete SeneBlends looks to suit your unique style and personality!

Concealer

MakeSense Foundation

BrowSense

EyeSense

ShadowSense

Base

Blending

Accent

LashSense

LinerSense

LipSense

Layer 1

Layer 2

Layer 3

LipSense Gloss

BlushSense

Base

Contouring

Highlighter

Translucid Bronzer

Translucid Powder

Concealer

MakeSense Foundation

BrowSense

EyeSense

ShadowSense

Base

Blending

Accent

LashSense

LinerSense

LipSense

Layer 1

Layer 2

Layer 3

LipSense Gloss

BlushSense

Base

Contouring

Highlighter

Translucid Bronzer

Translucid Powder

Concealer

MakeSense Foundation

BrowSense

EyeSense

ShadowSense

Base

Blending

Accent

LashSense

LinerSense

LipSense

Layer 1

Layer 2

Layer 3

LipSense Gloss

BlushSense

Base

Contouring

Highlighter

Translucid Bronzer

Translucid Powder

Practice creating your own complete SeneBlends looks to suit your unique style and personality!

Concealer _____

MakeSense Foundation _____

BrowSense _____

EyeSense _____

ShadowSense _____

Base _____

Blending _____

Accent _____

LashSense _____

LinerSense _____

LipSense _____

Layer 1 _____

Layer 2 _____

Layer 3 _____

LipSense Gloss _____

BlushSense _____

Base _____

Contouring _____

Highlighter _____

Translucid Bronzer _____

Translucid Powder _____

Concealer _____

MakeSense Foundation _____

BrowSense _____

EyeSense _____

ShadowSense _____

Base _____

Blending _____

Accent _____

LashSense _____

LinerSense _____

LipSense _____

Layer 1 _____

Layer 2 _____

Layer 3 _____

LipSense Gloss _____

BlushSense _____

Base _____

Contouring _____

Highlighter _____

Translucid Bronzer _____

Translucid Powder _____

Concealer _____

MakeSense Foundation _____

BrowSense _____

EyeSense _____

ShadowSense _____

Base _____

Blending _____

Accent _____

LashSense _____

LinerSense _____

LipSense _____

Layer 1 _____

Layer 2 _____

Layer 3 _____

LipSense Gloss _____

BlushSense _____

Base _____

Contouring _____

Highlighter _____

Translucid Bronzer _____

Translucid Powder _____

A Little Extra Help

SeneDerm Solutions: Your Beauty Problems Solved

SeneDerm Solutions is a complete line of specialized treatment products that are mostly derived from plant peptide complexes and serve as effective "Solutions" for an array of targeted specific skin and personal care needs. Whether you have dark circles, age-spots, or wrinkles, you will find a SeneDerm Solution that is right for you.

 Solutions products are formulated with SenePlex Complex for increased cellular renewal.

Anti-Wrinkle Treatment

Clinically proven to visibly reduce the depth and shadows of light and medium size wrinkles (by an average of 34% up to 63%), making skin's texture smoother and younger-looking. Contains an advanced formulation including natural ingredients proven to relax wrinkles, stimulate cell production, and restore proper moisture content with regular use. Effective ingredients include:

- Anti-Wrinkle Complex- calms nerves and relaxes muscles
- Camellia Senensis Leaf- protects from collagen breakdown

Dark Circle Under Eye Treatment

Excessive under eye darkening and visible bagging prematurely ages eyes. Correct it with this effective blend of ingredients to reduce the appearance of darkening, and tighten loose skin in the sensitive area under the eyes. You'll be a bright-eyed beauty in no time. The powerful and effective ingredients include:

- Blend of ingredients including Suma Root extract, Ptychopetalum Olacoides, Bark/Stem, and Lilium Candidum flower extract that work to reduce under eye darkening.

LashExtend

Say goodbye to false eyelashes and expensive extensions by naturally and safely enhancing your gorgeous gaze with this non-drug lash lengthener. Results rival prescription treatments that cost over twice as much! Choose clear treatment for twice daily use or water resistant black or brown liquid liner for brilliantly lined eyes and luscious lashes in one easy step.

- SenePeptide - stimulates hair growth
- Chamomile Extract - anti-irritant with soothing properties
- White Tea Extract - powerful anti-oxidant

LipVolumizer

Plump up the volume and get lasting results of full, pouty lips without the use of irritants. The proprietary formula of LipVolumizer is based on the most advanced and natural lip plumping technologies, plumping lips from inside out. Lips will become noticeably smoother and fuller, while feathering and cracked lips are eliminated with continued use. LipVolumizer comes in clear for natural looking, plumped lips. Effective ingredients include:

- Volumizing Complex- proprietary blend of peptides and botanicals
- Kiss-Me-Quick Plant- helps boost collagen production and increase moisture

Polishing Exfoliator

Polish away rough, dry skin and impurities with this unique formula containing naturally exfoliating Vanuatu Volcanic Ash. A little goes a long way to gently but effectively buff skin to a luminous glow.

- Vanuatu Volcanic Ash - exfoliates dead cells and polishes skin
- Nangai Oil - deeply hydrates and soothes skin with moisture-enhancing triglycerides

Nangai Oil

Intensely moisturize and soothe dry skin with this luxurious, natural blend of exotic Nangai Oil and anti-aging ingredients. Found on the tropical island nation of Vanuatu, Nangai oil provides skin anti-inflammatory and deeply hydrating benefits.

- Triglycerides - essential fatty acids that help enhance your skin's ability to retain precious moisture
- SenePlex Complex - for increased cellular renewal

SeneBlends MUA Tip: "For really hydrated and healthy looking and feeling skin, take a few drops of Nangai Oil and mix it with Body Lotion before applying it to the skin on your body. This will leave your skin so soft and moist!" - Deb Sell, MUA of the Month

Fooops™ & Ooops!® Color Removers

For removing our long-lasting cosmetics, you'll need these wonderful removers. They are specially formulated to easily take off SenseCosmetics, but also be gently moisturizing and provide the same anti-aging benefits found throughout the SenseCosmetics line.

Fooops™ SenseCosmetics Color Remover

Remove long-lasting SenseCosmetics quickly and easily with this unique, easy-to-use formula that activates when shaken. It gently whisks away all makeup including waterproof LashSense mascara, while conditioning and refreshing the skin. Ideal for all skin types, it leaves the face and eyes feeling cool and relaxed without an oily residue. Safe for contact wearers.

- SenePlex Complex – increased cellular renewal
- Arnica Flower – helps to restore suppleness
- Spirulina – protects from bacteria growth that can contribute to breakouts

LipSense Ooops! Remover

With Ooops!, mistakes are gone. A simple swipe will erase application errors, help to "lift" your long-lasting LipSense so you can change your shade with your outfit, or remove it at the end of the day. No rubbing required!

- Vitamins A, B, C & E- conditions, moisturizes and protects lips

SeneDerm BodyCare

SeneDerm anti-aging BodyCare encourages cellular renewal from head to toe. The skin on your body is thicker than that of your face, and requires more intense exfoliates and richer moisturizers to replenish moisture and protect form environmental hazards. This simple-to-use system will give you the smooth, radiant skin you've always wanted!

BodyCare products are formulated with SenePlex Complex for increased cellular renewal.

Advanced Hydration Body Lotion

Pamper your skin all over with rich, luxurious moisture and anti-aging protection from head-to-toe. Packed with advanced anti-aging technology and soothing botanicals, it intensely quenches skin with moisture, while increasing your skin's ability to retain water to help correct and prevent signs of aging.

The powerful and effective ingredients include:

- Sodium Hyaluronate- restores damaged cellular walls
- French Plum Oil- natural, non-greasy hydrating oil featuring a light, luxurious scent
- SenePlex+- for extremely advanced cellular renewal

SeneBlends MUA Tip: "Mix Advanced Hydration Body Lotion with Bronze BlushSense for the perfect tinted body moisturizer! Not only will it give your skin a tanned finish, but it also gives your skin a hydration treatment!"- Sheila Young, MUA of the Month

Hand Cream with Shea Butter

Extra care for hands to balance, maintain and seal in moisture, leaving no greasy feeling behind. A little goes a long way as it reactivates with water and rubbing throughout the day. The powerful and effective ingredients include:

- Shea Butter- rich moisturizer
- Cucumber- soothes and hydrates

Moisturizing Body Wash

The Body Wash is a rich, gentle, foaming gel that cleanses the entire body. While traditional soaps can dry and crack the skin, the Body Wash conditions and restores pH balance.

The powerful and effective ingredients include:

- Algae Extract- hydrates and softens skin
- Aloe Vera- soothes skin

Soothing Body Scrub

Exfoliating is important to keep skin smooth and healthy because it allows for better moisture absorption. The Body Scrub is gentle, yet highly effective and is made for all skin types.

The powerful and effective ingredients include:

- Vanuatu Volcanic Ash- exfoliates dead cells
- Aloe Vera- soothes skin

Shea Butter Body Cream

Pamper your skin with rich emollient moisture. Experience immediate dry skin relief and diminish visible signs of aging. The powerful and effective ingredients include:

- Shea Butter- helps skin retain moisture and can aid in reducing scars

"I use Shea Butter Body Cream every night on my feet, my hands and on my lips over the LipVolumizer. I keep both on my night stand always so I don't forget!" -Jeri Taylor-Swade

Detoxifying Mask

This creamy, non-drying natural mineral and botanical-based treatment mask gently removes impurities from pores to reveal smoother and softer-looking skin. It helps to rid skin of dead cells and works to soothe and diminish redness. Suitable for all skin types, including acne-prone.

- Green Tea & Arnica flower – soothes and counteracts redness
- Kaolin Clay – absorbs toxins
- Volcanic Ash – gentle exfoliator